PRACTICE MAKES PERFECT

Preparation for State Reading Assessments

Prestwick House

P.O. Box 658 Clayton, Delaware 19938

www.prestwickhouse.com

Senior Editor: Paul Moliken

Author: Sondra Y. Abel

Editor: Mary C. Beardsley

Reviewing Teachers: Barbara Bretherick, Wellington, FL
Catherine O. Routh, Helena, GA

Cover Design: Larry Knox

Production: Jerry Clark

Prestwick House

P.O. Box 658 • Clayton, Delaware 19938

Tel: 1.800.932.4593

Fax: 1.888.718.9333

Web: www.prestwickhouse.com

ISBN 978-1-58049-317-8

PRACTICE MAKES PERFECT LEVEL 8

Preparation for State Reading Assessments

Table of Contents

Preparation for
State Reading Assessments

Introduction to the Student

How to Take a Reading Comprehension Test

Taking a reading comprehension test does not have to be a stressful event. The following tips and methods can be used to make your test-taking efforts more effective and your results more accurate.

FOCUS:

When you read a comprehension passage, you should try to identify the following:

- main idea
- author's attitude or tone
- author's purpose

Many comprehension questions focus on your ability to determine what the author is trying to say and why he or she is saying it. Think about whether the author is biased: Does he or she support, criticize, or remain objective about the subject? What clues show the writer's attitude?

While you read, you should imagine yourself as the test writer.

- Which pieces of information do you think are important?
- Is the passage about a person or a group of people?
- What is that person's or group's message to the world?
- What questions would you write about the passage?

When you come across a point that stands out, make a mental note of it. Ask yourself why the author included it. Information that seems to have a special purpose often shows up in the questions.

TIPS:

In order to determine an author's attitude toward the subject, look for emotionally charged words, such as *tragically, sadly, unfortunately, surprisingly, amazingly, justly,* etc. These words indicate an author's bias—whether the author sides with or against the subject of the passage. Simple words tell you a lot about the author's feelings.

Frequently, you are asked to identify the main idea of a passage. These types of questions do not always use the words *main idea*. They may ask for the most appropriate title or the statement with which the author would most likely agree or disagree. Pick the answer that is true for the entire passage. If no choice relates to the entire selection, choose the answer that is supported by most of the passage.

You will also encounter questions that ask you to define a word or find the most appropriate synonym. These questions check your ability to use context clues, not your vocabulary knowledge. Sometimes, you will find more than one seemingly correct answer, but when you look at the word as it is used in the paragraph, you can choose the best synonym for the situation.

Some questions are open-ended and require you to write an answer. You must write two to four complete sentences to answer these types of questions. The person who scores your answer will look for you to explain yourself, so be sure to support your opinion with details from the passage.

Finally, when it comes to taking timed tests, many people feel pressured to race through the work so that they complete all of it. Remember, though, that careful reading cannot be rushed. So, what can you do? When you cannot decide the answer to a question, skip it and come back to it after you have answered the rest of the questions for that passage. You may even find the answer when you are working on other questions. If you still cannot answer it, make your best guess and move on, rather than spend too much time trying to figure out one question, leaving yourself insufficient time to answer the rest accurately.

Some people suggest reading the questions before you read the passage so that you know what information you need. If this works for you, that is terrific! For many people, however, this uses valuable time and results in too much information to remember. This breaks their concentration, and they cannot focus on what they read. If you cannot focus on both the questions and the reading at one time, read the passage first, concentrating on what you read. If you need to look back at the passage to answer the questions, go ahead and do so. The point to be made here is that you should work in a manner that is comfortable for you. When you find a technique that works for you, use it!

REMEMBER THESE THREE EXTREMELY IMPORTANT POINTS:

1. **Read the directions and questions carefully!**
   Look for tricky words, such as *not, always, true, opposite,* etc. These words greatly affect the answer to the question.

2. **If you cannot remember what you just read, read it again, and pay attention to it!**

3. **Always read all the answer choices!**
   You may choose the wrong answer and miss the correct one entirely if you stop reading once you think you have found the answer. There may be a better choice further down the list, and you will miss it if you do not read it.

Model Passage

The following model passage demonstrates effective use of the reading tips and strategies. You will see that there are underlined words and phrases in the passage and notes in the margins. The notes in the margins refer to the underlined portions of the passage and serve as examples of the way you should think about the passage. These notes include questions you should ask yourself or comments you should make to yourself as you read.

The Railroads Connect

On May 10, 1869, the Transcontinental Railroad was finally connected after years of hard work and confusion, but the celebration of the "Wedding of the Rails" was plagued by disorder and misunderstanding.[1]

Of course, the real story is a comedy of errors.[2] First,[3] the actual location of the event was Promontory Summit, Utah, but since this was not on the map, the press reported that it occurred at Promontory Point; therefore, postcards, souvenirs, and even textbooks to this day bear the name of the incorrect location. Second, on May 4, 1869,[4] the president of the Central Pacific Railroad, Leland Stanford, revealed to his friend, David Hewes, that no commemorative item had been made for the event. Upset by this fact, Hewes attempted to have a solid gold spike made, but after failing to find someone to finance it, he had $400 worth of his own gold melted and cast[5] as the "Golden Spike," which was then **engraved**[6] for the occasion. Three other spikes were also made for the event. The next problem arose when the event had to be postponed because **disgruntled**[6] workers and poor weather conditions delayed the arrival of officials from the Union Pacific Railroad. Finally, on May 10, 1869, the officials from both the Union Pacific and the Central Pacific railroads **convened** for the celebration. A special laurelwood railroad tie was laid in place at the junction, and the specially made spikes were dropped into pre-drilled holes. Not one of them was actually hammered into place.[7] Then, the laurelwood tie and spikes were replaced with a standard tie and regular iron spikes. The last spike and the hammer were connected to the telegraph line so that the entire nation could hear[8] the

[1]This passage will be about the disorder of the "Wedding of the Rails" celebration.

[2]What are the funny errors?

[3]The points are organized. The word *first* tells me to look for *second*, etc. Look for *next* and *finally*.

[4]Wow, that is only six days before the ceremony.

[5]Wow, $400 of his own gold! Why? What kind of question could the test ask about this?

[6]I should look at the context of these boldfaced words. What do they mean?

[7]Those spikes were just dropped in the holes!

[8]This was a huge event if the telegraph was going to relay the sound.

"Wedding of the Rails."[9] The sound of the hammer hitting the spike would then travel across the country through the telegraph line. Leland Stanford was given the first swing, but he missed[10] the spike and hit the wooden tie. Thomas Durant, vice president of the Union Pacific Railroad, swung at the spike, but missed entirely. In the end, a railroad employee hammered in the final tie,[10] and the telegraph operator sent the message to the country: "D-O-N-E."

Not so surprisingly, when the fiftieth anniversary celebration was scheduled, not one person showed up.[11] Maybe they all went to Promontory Point.

[9] The name of the event is mentioned again. This must be important.

[10] That is funny—after all of the problems, the important people who were supposed to hammer the spike could not do it.

[11] That is funny, too. I cannot believe no one showed up. It seems as if no one cared.

1. Which of the following best states the author's purpose?

A. to make fun of the Transcontinental Railroad

B. to make an accurate portrayal of an important event in railroad history

C. to explain the importance of the Golden Spike

D. to describe how history books sometimes contain incorrect information

(B) The author accurately describes the confusion and mishaps surrounding the "Wedding of the Rails" celebration. All other answer choices are merely supporting points in the passage.

2. Which of the following would be the best title for this passage?

A. The Golden Spike Disaster

B. Where the Railroads Meet

C. Leland Stanford's Spike

D. The Wedding of the Rails

(D) The passage is about the entire "Wedding of the Rails" ceremony. After all, the ceremony's title is mentioned twice in the passage, making it significant information and appropriate for the title. Although the event was riddled with errors, it would not be considered a disaster. Finally, the passage does not focus solely on Leland Stanford's spike or where the event occurred.

3. Which of the following did not contribute to the confusion on May 10, 1869?

A. the telegraph operator
B. poor weather conditions
C. last-minute planning
D. uncertainty about the location

(A) The telegraph operator did not make any errors. The poor weather postponed officials, last-minute planning required a friend to donate his own gold for the commemorative spike, and uncertainty about the location led to incorrect information.

4. As used in the passage, the word *engraved* most nearly means

A. molded.
B. decorated.
C. transported.
D. purchased.

(B) If the spike was engraved for the occasion, it must have been decorated to show its commemorative purpose. Molded is not the answer because the passage already stated that the gold was melted and cast. Although the spike would have to be transported, the context is discussing the making of the spike, not the shipping of the spike. Finally, the gold was already purchased, since it belonged to Hewes.

5. Based on the information provided in the passage, what can you infer is the reason for David Hewes's melting his own gold to make the spike?

A. He was angry that no one would help him.
B. He wanted to become famous for his contribution to the Transcontinental Railroad.
C. He could find no one willing to pay for or donate the gold.
D. He had more gold than he needed, so he was willing to give some away.

(C) Hewes tried to find someone to finance a rail but was unsuccessful. Had he found someone willing to pay or donate at least something, then he would not have had to use his own resources. Since he looked for someone to finance a golden rail instead of financing it himself, we can infer that he did not have an overabundance of gold. There are no clues to imply he was searching for fame. Finally, the passage states that he was upset that there was no item made to commemorate the event, but no mention was made of his being angry at finding no one willing to help.

6. ***Answer the following question using complete sentences:***
Why does the author call the "Wedding of the Rails" a "comedy of errors"?

The event is humorous because it was a major celebration of the uniting of the country's rails, which was a massive undertaking, and almost everything that could go wrong did. Railroad officials arrived late because their workers were unhappy, the commemorative spike was not even hammered in, and a railroad employee, not any of the officials who organized the celebration, completed the actual connection of the rails. As a final taunt, no one showed up for the fiftieth anniversary celebration.

DIRECTIONS: *Read the passage and answer the questions that follow it.*

The Origins of Uncle Sam

SOME PEOPLE CLAIM that the original Uncle Sam, the now-famous image appearing on posters proclaiming, "I want YOU for U.S. Army!" was Sam Wilson, a meat packer in Troy, New York. Wilson supplied the U.S. military with meat during the War of 1812. Since shipments were marked "U.S.," the soldiers joked that the meat was from "Uncle Sam." Soon, Wilson's employees heard the joke and spread it through the company. In this way, the initials U.S. gave way to Uncle Sam as the personified version of the United States government. While many people accept this version as the origin of Uncle Sam, others refute the claim. After all, this story was not printed until many years after the event, and the passage of time allows for misinterpretations and flawed memories. The United States Congress, however, did give Sam Wilson the credit for Uncle Sam in 1961, when they issued this resolution: "Resolved by the Senate (the House of Representatives concurring) that the Congress salutes 'Uncle Sam' Wilson of Troy, New York, as the **progenitor** of America's National symbol of 'Uncle Sam.' "

Thomas Nast, a political cartoonist, created Uncle Sam's image. Sam is often depicted as an elderly man who wears a top hat, which features stars and stripes, a coat (with the colors red, white, and blue), and striped pants. Early references to Uncle Sam appeared in newspapers that were opposed to the War of 1812. It is possible that Uncle Sam's image was used by people as a way to criticize the government. By creating a person, they would have someone to mock and receive their anger. The most famous version of Uncle Sam, the one on the Army recruiting posters from WWI, was created by James Montgomery Flagg. Today, Uncle Sam is seen as an honorable figure and is often treated with respect when portrayed in the U.S. He is also used in political and patriotic campaigns, such as those asking citizens to join the military.

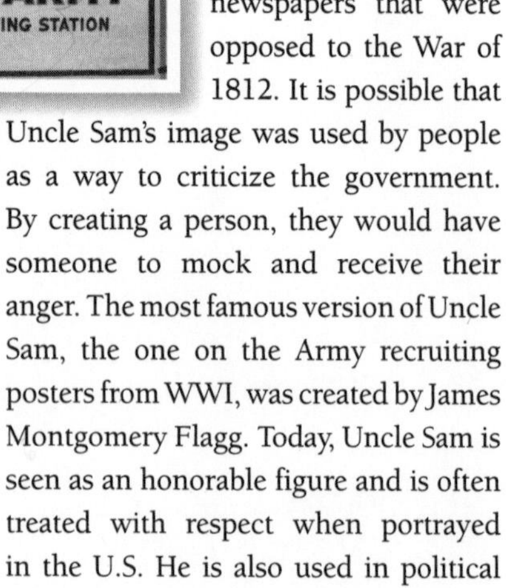

QUESTIONS

1. **Which one of the following best states the author's purpose?**
   - **A.** to discuss the influence Uncle Sam had during the War of 1812
   - **B.** to explain why Uncle Sam is a well-known world symbol
   - **C.** to show how Uncle Sam became a popular figure
   - **D.** to describe the career of Sam Wilson

2. **How has the image of Uncle Sam changed over the years?**
   - **A.** Uncle Sam's image had been used honorably, but now, the image is used in political cartoons to criticize the government.
   - **B.** Uncle Sam's image had been used in political cartoons to criticize the government, but now, the image is used honorably.
   - **C.** Uncle Sam's image was originally the picture of Uncle Sam Wilson, the meat packer, but the picture has changed over the years.
   - **D.** Uncle Sam's image is used today the same way it was used two hundred years ago.

3. **Which of the following best describes the reason for the first paragraph?**
   - **A.** It describes New York's role during the War of 1812.
   - **B.** It describes the original portrayal of Uncle Sam.
   - **C.** It describes Sam Wilson's possible role as Uncle Sam.
   - **D.** It mentions how Congress identified Uncle Sam.

4. **As used in the passage, the word *progenitor* most nearly means**
   - **A.** originator.
   - **B.** caricature.
   - **C.** ancestor.
   - **D.** cartoonist.

5. **According to the passage, which statement is true?**
   - **A.** Sam Wilson was in the military during the War of 1812.
   - **B.** The Congress has yet to recognize the origin of Uncle Sam officially.
   - **C.** Uncle Sam is used only as a symbol to criticize the government.
   - **D.** Uncle Sam is often depicted with a top hat.

6. ***Answer the following question using complete sentences:***
   The author states that Uncle Sam is treated with respect when used by Americans today. How might enemy countries use the figure of Uncle Sam?

DIRECTIONS: *Read the passage and answer the questions that follow it.*

Celiac Disease

IMAGINE NOT BEING able to consume foods that are made with wheat flour, oats, barley, or rye. Most processed foods contain these items. A person who has celiac disease, also called celiac sprue or gluten intolerance, cannot eat breads, pastas, or pastries made with regular flours. Celiac disease is a genetic disorder that affects up to 1 in 133 Americans. Approximately 2.18 million Americans suffer from this disease, but often go undiagnosed because doctors and specialists still consider it to be a "rare" disease. In addition, the symptoms of this disease are similar to other gastrointestinal disorders; therefore, it is often diagnosed as a more well-known disease. It is possible to test for the disorder by taking a blood test or by having a **biopsy** performed on the intestines. In the biopsy diagnosis, the extracted tissue allows doctors to accurately determine if the person has celiac disease.

Symptoms of the disease vary among individuals. Those with a severe sensitivity can experience painful gas and diarrhea, weight loss, and malnutrition. Other symptoms include nutrient deficiencies such as anemia. Individuals with the disease experience these symptoms because the body recognizes gluten, a protein in the grain, as a toxin. Gluten damages the villi (which help absorb nutrients) in the intestines. Once damaged, the intestines create the above-mentioned symptoms, and over time, the intestines cease to absorb essential nutrients. Studies have shown that individuals who continue to eat gluten increase their chances of gastrointestinal cancer by forty percent.

There is no cure for celiac disease. The only way to treat it is to adhere to a gluten-free diet for life. Unfortunately, it is not a typical food allergy that individuals will simply outgrow; they contend with it for life. On the other hand, more specialty grocery stores and some restaurants are now providing gluten-free foods.

QUESTIONS

1. **According to the passage, which of the following is false?**
   - **A.** Celiac disease is a rare illness in America.
   - **B.** Celiac disease restricts people from eating gluten.
   - **C.** Celiac disease affects approximately 2.18 million Americans.
   - **D.** Celiac disease is frequently misdiagnosed as another intestinal disorder.

2. **Which of the following would be the best title for this passage?**
   - **A.** Are You Gluten Intolerant?
   - **B.** Gluten Is Your Friend
   - **C.** Celiac Intolerance—Cancer Cause
   - **D.** Intestinal Disorders Weaken People

3. **What is the primary purpose of the second paragraph?**
   - **A.** It examines how nutrient deficiencies affect the body.
   - **B.** It describes the effects of gluten on an individual with celiac sprue.
   - **C.** It explains why the disease goes undiagnosed.
   - **D.** It describes the purpose of the villi within the intestines.

4. **Which of the following best describes the problem of celiac disease?**
   - **A.** Celiac sprue is a genetic disorder that affects only those of European descent.
   - **B.** Gluten intolerance is a rare disease that affects a small percentage of the American population.
   - **C.** In individuals with celiac disease, the intestines recognize gluten as a toxin.
   - **D.** Individuals with celiac disease cannot eat any processed foods.

5. **As used in the passage, the word *biopsy* most nearly means**
   - **A.** illustration.
   - **B.** removal.
   - **C.** shrinking.
   - **D.** sample.

6. ***Answer the following question using complete sentences:***
   How might having such a disease affect your lifestyle?

DIRECTIONS: *Read the passage and answer the questions that follow it.*

Bloodletting

BLOODLETTING, OR WITHDRAWING large quantities of blood from patients, was a popular medical healing practice from ancient times until the nineteenth century. Erasistratus, an ancient Greek, believed that many diseases were caused by an overabundance of blood; therefore, releasing it could cure a patient. Once it was discovered that the veins and arteries were filled with blood instead of air, bloodletting gained great popularity in Greece. Galen, who made the discovery, believed that blood did not circulate through the body. He also claimed that the body's balance depended on four humors: blood, phlegm, black bile, and yellow bile. Illnesses resulted from an imbalance in one of the humors, and bloodletting was considered a means of restoring balance to the humors. Galen created a complex system for bloodletting based on several factors, including the patient's age and the weather. Blood was released from certain locations depending on the patient's disease or symptoms. The more severe the disease, the greater the amount of blood shed.

Physicians recommended bloodletting to cure many diseases, and the practice would be performed by a surgeon or barber. The most common method for extracting blood was called phlebotomy or venesection. In this procedure, blood was taken from large veins, especially those in the arm or neck. (Today, phlebotomy refers to the procedure of drawing blood for testing or storage.) Otherwise, practitioners would puncture arteries or use syringes, special vacuums, or leeches to draw blood. When the patient fainted, then it was determined that enough blood had been let.

Bloodletting was popular throughout Greece, Egypt, and Mesopotamia. As the popularity spread, religious groups also started bloodletting. Catholics, for example, practiced bloodletting on certain saints' days. Until the Middle Ages, bloodletting was used as a method to cure most **ailments**. During the sixteenth century, physicians began questioning the effectiveness of bloodletting, and debates continued until the nineteenth century. Although bloodletting was extremely popular in the U.S., it is now rarely used.

QUESTIONS

1. **Why did the author write this passage?**
   A. to inform the reader about an ancient medical practice
   B. to explain why some diseases have no cure
   C. to explain why bloodletting was popular
   D. to inform the reader about Greek contributions to medicine

2. **Which of the following would be the best title for this passage?**
   A. Bloodshed
   B. Phlebotomy
   C. Doctors Versus Vampires
   D. Bloody Medicine

3. **Which of the following is the main reason for the final paragraph?**
   A. It describes the different methods of bloodletting.
   B. It explains why bloodletting is no longer a popular treatment.
   C. It explains how bloodletting gained and lost popularity.
   D. It describes the various cultures that practiced bloodletting.

4. **As used in the passage, the word *ailments* most nearly means**
   A. deformities.
   B. sicknesses.
   C. patients.
   D. fevers.

5. **Based on the passage, what can be inferred about bloodletting?**
   A. Special devices were invented for bloodletting.
   B. Bloodletting was done only on patients with severe illnesses.
   C. Blood was extracted in small quantities only.
   D. The practice of bloodletting has been abolished.

6. ***Answer the following question using complete sentences:***
   Why might bloodletting have been so popular throughout the centuries?

DIRECTIONS: *Read the passage and answer the questions that follow it.*

Protecting the Border

AMERICA IS A LAND COMPOSED almost entirely of immigrants. In fact, all those not of Native American descent are immigrants. Although this country has a reputation for welcoming people into the "land of opportunity," limitations must be made on how many people (and from where) may enter annually. Otherwise, certain areas of the country would face various problems, overpopulation and social services support being perhaps the most crucial. Such limitations have caused a sharp spike in illegal immigration. A major source of illegal immigration occurs through the U.S.–Mexico border, despite the efforts of the U.S. Border Patrol.

Many have debated the proper ways to handle illegal immigration. In attempts to curb the number of illegal entries, the Minuteman Project began in April 2005 in Arizona. A group of approximately 1,000 private citizens joined with the Border Patrol in watching a twenty-three-mile stretch of the southern Arizona border. The volunteers alert Border Patrol but cannot make any physical contact with immigrants entering illegally. Jim Gilchrist, the group's principal director, describes the group as "a citizen's Neighborhood Watch on our border." The Project is expected to expand to the U.S.–Canadian border with volunteers stretching from Washington to New Hampshire.

Many of the Minutemen are retired firefighters, police officers, or business professionals who view Minuteman service as a patriotic duty, protecting Americans from illegal aliens, potential terrorists, and **contraband** that cross the borders daily. They have gained tremendous support from the public and political officials. Former Governor Arnold Schwarzenegger, for example, praised their efforts and welcomed them to patrol the border between California and Mexico. Although they have gained support, they have also endured much criticism. Mexico's president has criticized the group's actions and lack of credentials. Many members of law enforcement and concerned citizens fear the group could lead to vigilante violence. Critics have claimed that some members are Neo-Nazi white supremacists, since groups such as the National Alliance openly supported the group and have posted racist flyers around the Project's events. According to the Minuteman Project's philosophy, however, they are simply there to do the job the government should be doing.

QUESTIONS

1. **Why did the author write this passage?**
   A. to inform the reader about the dangers of illegal aliens
   B. to explain why illegal immigration is a problem
   C. to describe a program in place to stop illegal immigration
   D. to explain how the Border Patrol is ineffective

2. **Why is illegal immigration a concern?**
   A. Limits must be set on immigration for the well-being of all involved.
   B. America simply has no more room for immigrants.
   C. There is not ample housing and employment for those who immigrate here.
   D. Americans should not be allowed to emigrate to other countries.

3. **Which of the following best describes the reason for the final paragraph?**
   A. It proves the Minutemen are white supremacists.
   B. It describes different views of the Project.
   C. It explains why the group is gaining popularity.
   D. It describes the mission of the Minuteman Project.

4. **As used in the passage, the word *contraband* most nearly means**
   A. ethnic items.
   B. dangerous weapons.
   C. valuable goods.
   D. illegal items.

5. **Which best describes the Minuteman Project?**
   A. It is a vigilante group that acts violently against immigrants.
   B. It is a volunteer group that assists the Border Patrol.
   C. It is a large group of demonstrators who rally in Arizona.
   D. It is a paid group that informs Border Patrol of illegal aliens.

6. ***Answer the following question using complete sentences:***
   Why would the government allow the Minuteman Project to patrol the border when there is an established Border Patrol already in existence?

DIRECTIONS: *Read the passage and answer the questions that follow it.*

Stonehenge

ONE OF BRITAIN'S MOST intriguing architectural mysteries, Stonehenge, is a circular group of standing stones resting on Salisbury Plain in southern England. The arrangement measures 300 feet in diameter. While the origins are uncertain, one of the theories proposes that construction on Stonehenge began around 3000 B.C., during the Neolithic Age by an ancient group of people called the Beaker Folk. Stonehenge was completed in three phases. The first phase, around 3100 B.C., consisted of wooden circles that were surrounded by a ditch and bank. The people dug the ditch with animal bones and deer antlers, which have been discovered by excavators. The second phase, around 2500 B.C., was built from blue stones. These stones, each weighting around five tons, were dragged from the Prescelli Mountains and floated on rafts up the Avon River. Before this phase was complete, the stones were rearranged around 2300 B.C. Then, sandstones were brought and hammered to size. The placement of these stones is considered the third stage. The completed Stonehenge features an egg-shaped center and an Altar Stone.

Many myths and legends exist to explain the origins and uses of Stonehenge in ancient times. For many years, people thought that Stonehenge was a temple used by druids or sorcerers. However, the druids did not arrive in Britain until around 250 B.C. Today, druids and other religious groups consider Stonehenge a sacred site of worship. Because of the **precise** positions of the stones, it may have been used as an observatory to predict eclipses and observe the positions of the sun and moon. UFO sightings have occurred at Stonehenge, leading some people to claim that the site is used for alien landings. While many theories exist, the latest one indicates that Stonehenge was used as the burial grounds for a royal family that ruled the area since prehistoric times.

QUESTIONS

1. **Which of the following would be the best title for the passage?**
   A. The Mystery of Stonehenge
   B. Stone Formations
   C. Stonehenge: Ancient Observatory
   D. Neolithic Creations

2. **Why did the author write this passage?**
   A. to describe the druids
   B. to describe the legends of Stonehenge
   C. to explain how Stonehenge could not have been built without machinery
   D. to explain how and why Stonehenge was built

3. **According to the passage, how was Stonehenge constructed?**
   A. Blue stones from the Prescelli Mountains were placed in a circular formation.
   B. Stonehenge was made of wood and stones by the druids.
   C. Stonehenge was made of timber and stones in three phases.
   D. Ditches were made from bones after blue stones were put into place.

4. **As used in the passage, the word *precise* most nearly means**
   A. magical.
   B. random.
   C. specific.
   D. geographic.

5. **According to the passage, which statement is true?**
   A. Stonehenge was completed in four phases.
   B. Beaker Folk constructed Stonehenge.
   C. Stonehenge may have been used as an observatory.
   D. Christians use Stonehenge as a center for worship.

6. ***Answer the following question using complete sentences:***
   Why was Stonehenge constructed?

DIRECTIONS: *Read the passage and answer the questions that follow it.*

Seahorses

ALTHOUGH MANY PEOPLE imagine seahorses as large enough to ride with a harness, probably because a well-known superhero does so in a cartoon, seahorses are actually small fish, ranging from six-tenths of an inch to over twelve inches in length. They live in temperate and tropical oceans around the world. The seahorse has a dorsal fin and pectoral fins near the gills by its head. Because the seahorse changes its color to match its environment, it is a master of **camouflage** and is extremely difficult to photograph in its natural habitat. A seahorse is easily identifiable by its head, which has a long snout like a horse. The seahorse swims in an upright position and moves forward by beating its fins quickly like a bird flapping its wings. While it is resting, it wraps its curled tail around seaweed to serve as an anchor.

Seahorses are one of the few species in which the male carries the fertilized eggs. During mating, the seahorses wrap their tails together and appear to dance. During the embrace, the female deposits the eggs into the male's pouch using her ovipositor. The male fertilizes the eggs and carries them while they feed and develop. Two to four weeks later, depending on the particular species and the temperature of the water, the male gives birth by twisting and writhing his body and pumping his tail repeatedly until the babies, called fry, emerge.

These unique fish have become endangered recently due to many factors. The seahorse is used in traditional Chinese herbology, a practice that uses herbs and other natural elements to try to cure illnesses. Over 20 million seahorses are caught and sold for herbology alone. Others are caught accidentally in fishing nets; some are sold as souvenirs. Still more seahorses are losing their habitats because of human interference. Although these fish are fascinating and unique, their continued existence is not safe until they become better protected.

QUESTIONS

1. Which of the following best states the author's purpose?

A. to describe the unique characteristics of the seahorse
B. to inform the reader about an extinct species
C. to explain how seahorses mate
D. to explain herbology involving seahorses

2. Which of the following would be the best title for this passage?

A. Transparent Creatures
B. The Seahorses
C. Seahorses Aren't Fish
D. The Unique Seahorse

3. As used in the passage, the word *camouflage* most nearly means

A. blinding.
B. concealment.
C. flattening.
D. trouble.

4. What is the purpose of the last paragraph?

A. It defines herbology.
B. It explains a popular use for seahorses.
C. It explains why the seahorse is endangered.
D. It shows how humans are destroying ocean life.

5. Which best describes the appearance of seahorses?

A. Seahorses are brightly colored fish that have long faces, like horses.
B. Seahorses are tiny fish with long faces and straight tails.
C. Seahorses are transparent fish that swim upside down.
D. Seahorses are color-changing fish with horse-like faces.

6. Which of the following best describes the birthing behavior of seahorses?

A. Seahorses entwine their tails while the female deposits her eggs into the male. He gives birth several weeks later.
B. The male rapidly pumps his tail and makes noises while giving birth.
C. Seahorses entwine their tails while the male fertilizes the female's eggs. She gives birth two weeks later.
D. After the male deposits his eggs, the female gives birth two weeks later by rapidly pumping her tail.

DIRECTIONS: *Read the passage and answer the questions that follow it.*

An Influential Talk Show Host

Oprah Winfrey's successful media career has made her the first African American woman to become a billionaire. Although she now lives on a forty-two acre estate in California, called "the Promised Land," Oprah did not always enjoy such a fabulous lifestyle. In fact, she was born on January 29, 1954, in Kosciusko, Mississippi, to a very poor family. Her parents, Vernita Lee (a housemaid) and Vernon Winfrey (a soldier) were unmarried teenagers when Oprah was born. Oprah's birth name was actually Orpah. This name comes from a Moabite woman in the biblical book of *Ruth*. After Oprah's birth, her mother moved north for better job prospects. Oprah spent the next six years living with her grandmother. She then returned to her mother, who was still living in **dire** poverty. Vernita made Oprah's overalls from potato sacks and gave her a corncob doll as a toy. After suffering from repeated incidents of abuse, Oprah went to live with her father in Nashville, Tennessee, at the age of fourteen. There, she worked hard and earned honors in school, receiving a full scholarship to Tennessee State University, where she studied speech and performing arts.

Before getting her own talk show, *The Oprah Winfrey Show*, in 1986, Oprah worked in local media and broadcasting stations in Nashville, Baltimore, and Chicago. Before she retired from it, Oprah's one-hour show was watched by 21 million viewers per week, and aired in 150 countries. While episodes sometimes focused on celebrities, many dealt with important social issues and featured guests who were suffering from poverty and unfortunate accidents. Oprah has created her own production company, called "Harpo Productions." In addition, she co-founded *Oxygen*, a television network channel for women. She also has her own book club and a lifestyle magazine named *O*. Having starred in several films, Winfrey has developed a successful career as an actress, too. Oprah has greatly influenced culture and highlighted important social issues. Because of her amazing popularity, she will likely continue to do so for years to come, serving as a shining example of perseverance and determination.

QUESTIONS

1. **Which of the following best states the author's purpose?**
   - **A.** to inform the reader about Oprah's acting career
   - **B.** to inform the reader about *The Oprah Winfrey Show*
   - **C.** to describe Oprah's personal life
   - **D.** to describe Oprah's career

2. **Which of the following best states the message the author is trying to communicate?**
   - **A.** Oprah's life teaches many lessons about making money and getting away from a life of struggle.
   - **B.** Oprah's life teaches how a person can join a better social class and succeed in show business.
   - **C.** Oprah's life teaches the importance of hard work and concern for the condition of others.
   - **D.** Oprah's life teaches many lessons about trusting in others to make life's important decisions.

3. **Which of the following statements best describes the reason for the final paragraph?**
   - **A.** It describes Oprah's involvement in different media.
   - **B.** It informs the reader about the people who appear on Oprah's show.
   - **C.** It describes Oprah's popularity around the globe.
   - **D.** It names Oprah's production studio.

4. **Which of the following best describes Oprah's career?**
   - **A.** Oprah is a popular actor who is often a guest on television shows.
   - **B.** Oprah is an important talk show host and former journalist.
   - **C.** Oprah is a journalist who has her own book club and magazine.
   - **D.** Oprah appears on television stations that cater to female audiences.

5. **As used in the passage, the word *dire* most nearly means**
   - **A.** trivial.
   - **B.** unfortunate.
   - **C.** near.
   - **D.** terrible.

6. ***Answer the following question using complete sentences:***

   What can you infer is significant about the name of Oprah's production company?

DIRECTIONS: *Read the passage and answer the questions that follow it.*

Running of the Bulls

THE RUNNING OF THE BULLS, or "el encierro," is part of an annual nine-day festival in Pamplona, Spain. This celebration, which also features fireworks, parades, and religious ceremonies, is held in honor of the city's patron saint, San Fermin. The entire festival enjoys world-renown because of the running of the bulls, which, ironically, takes only about three minutes, but is the most popular event. The running of the bulls begins each morning at 8:00. Six bulls from Spain's top breeding ranches are selected to run a half-mile stretch through enclosed streets. They run from Santo Domingo Street to the city's bullring; here, each bull will fight a matador in the afternoon.

The encierros can be dangerous to runners and bystanders because of the size of the crowd, the animals' **unpredictability**, and the runners' inexperience. The bulls, which have razor-sharp horns, have been bread to fight and can weigh over 1,300 pounds. For safety reasons, security guards and first-aid assistants oversee the running. While runners are encouraged to keep a safe distance from the bulls, many believe that it is good luck to touch one. Above all, hurting the animals (even pulling their tails) is not permissible. Record-keeping began in 1924, and since then, many deaths and serious injuries have occurred. Runners are not the only ones who face injury, however. Because of their size and the cobbled stones on the streets, many bulls lose their footing and tumble.

By the 1800s, the running became a well-established tradition despite the fact that some opposed it. The event has made Pamplona famous. Ernest Hemingway, a famous writer, mentioned the city's tradition in his novel *The Sun Also Rises*, and as a result, the celebration's popularity skyrocketed. Spain officially recognized Hemingway for this contribution by naming a street in Pamplona after him: Avenida de Hemingway. Many tourists flock to Pamplona to view or participate in the event that Hemingway described. ⊙

QUESTIONS

1. **Which of the following best states the author's purpose?**
   A. to describe a religious ceremony that is held in Spain
   B. to explain why Pamplona is famous
   C. to mention a famous work of Ernest Hemingway
   D. to expose how animals are mistreated

2. **Which of the following would be the best title for this passage?**
   A. It Takes a Village
   B. El Encierro
   C. Ceremonies in Spain
   D. Running From Danger

3. **Which of the following are the most serious dangers runners might encounter?**
   A. crushing and fainting
   B. fainting and exhausting
   C. goring and crushing
   D. crowding and crushing

4. **As used in the passage, the word *unpredictability* means**
   A. intelligence.
   B. speed.
   C. stability.
   D. uncertainty.

5. **How did the running of the bulls become a popular event?**
   A. A famous writer described the event in his book.
   B. A famous journalist described the event in his articles.
   C. Throughout the years, more people have traveled to Pamplona.
   D. The bullfights have drawn large crowds.

6. ***Answer the following question using complete sentences:***
   How are the bulls treated during this celebration?

DIRECTIONS: *Read the passage and answer the questions that follow it.*

Langston Hughes

JUSTICE

That Justice is a blind goddess
Is a thing to which we black are wise:
Her bandage hides two **festering** sores
That once perhaps were eyes.
– Langston Hughes

LANGSTON HUGHES WAS BORN in Joplin, Missouri, in 1902, to an abolitionist family. Hughes started writing poetry in the eighth grade, but his father did not think it would make a practical career. Hughes's father offered to pay his son's tuition at Columbia University on the condition that he study engineering. Hughes accepted the offer, but quickly dropped out of the program to pursue his writing. Hughes's poems, short stories, and plays soon appeared in a variety of publications that promoted African American authors. In 1926, "The Negro Artist and the Racial Mountain," was published in the *Nation*, a newspaper founded by abolitionists. In the piece, Hughes said "Black poets" would rather be simply called "poets" instead of "Black poets." The term "Black poet" suggested that the author wanted to write like a white poet did.

In 1923, Hughes began a series of trips abroad to areas of Africa, Europe, and Russia. He also frequently visited Washington, D.C., and Harlem, a Manhattan neighborhood in New York City. During these trips, Hughes visited clubs to listen to blues and jazz music, which he incorporated into his poems. He moved to Washington, D.C. in 1925, but returned to Harlem the following year during the Harlem Renaissance. During this period, his writing took on a new rhythm and gained great popularity.

In 1929, Langston Hughes earned his bachelor's degree from Lincoln University in Pennsylvania, and in 1943, the school awarded him an honorary Doctor of Literature. He also received a Guggenheim Fellowship in 1935 and a Rosenwald Fellowship in 1940. Between the completion of his first book in 1926 and his death in 1967, Langston Hughes had written sixteen books of poetry, two novels, three collections of short stories, twenty plays, three autobiographies, dozens of articles, and too many other pieces to name.

QUESTIONS

1. **Which of the following statements would be the best title for this passage?**
   - **A.** Langston Hughes: Abolitionist at Heart
   - **B.** Writers of the Harlem Renaissance
   - **C.** Langston Hughes: Poet
   - **D.** The Life of Langston Hughes

2. **Which of the following best states the author's purpose?**
   - **A.** to examine an unsuccessful African American author in the 1900s
   - **B.** to prove parents are wrong about career choices
   - **C.** to show how traveling abroad expands horizons
   - **D.** to explain how a famous African American author achieved his success

3. **What is the purpose of the first paragraph?**
   - **A.** It describes how Hughes began his writing career.
   - **B.** It explains why Hughes went to college.
   - **C.** It gives details about Hughes's family life.
   - **D.** It shows the importance of education.

4. **As used in the passage, the word *festering* most nearly means**
   - **A.** gleaming.
   - **B.** rotting.
   - **C.** ugly.
   - **D.** healthy.

5. **According to the passage, what did Hughes use for inspiration?**
   - **A.** Hughes drew inspiration from traveling while on vacation.
   - **B.** Hughes drew inspiration from racial discrimination.
   - **C.** Hughes drew inspiration from his race and music.
   - **D.** Hughes drew inspiration from abolitionists.

6. ***Answer the following question using complete sentences:***
   What is Langston Hughes's message about justice in his poem?

DIRECTIONS: *Read the passage and answer the questions that follow it.*

Egypt's King Tut

THROUGHOUT HISTORY, various cultures have believed that mummies possess magical powers. Some thought that a mummy's power could be beneficial to humans. In fact, several Egyptian mummies were ground into powder and used for special healing purposes. In recent years, however, mummies have been associated with fatal curses. Since King Tut's tomb was opened, mummies have been considered magical enemies who seek **revenge** on those who enter their tombs.

According to legend, when Howard Carter opened King Tut's tomb on November 26, 1922, he found a tablet that said, "Death will slay with his wings whoever disturbs the peace of the pharaoh." But there is no record by photograph or sketch of this tablet. According to various legends, Carter found other items that were inscribed with curses from King Tut.

The media began telling stories about King Tut's curse when Lord Carnarvon, the man who funded the discovery, died a year after the tomb was opened. Carnarvon had been ill, but his condition became progressively worse after the opening. The media seized the story and claimed that King Tut wanted revenge. Although Carnarvon died, Howard Carter, the first one to enter the tomb, lived; he spent over a decade recording the artifacts he found in the tomb. In that time, others associated with the excavation of the tomb died mysteriously, and their deaths were attributed to Tut's curse as well.

Many people believed King Tut's curse to be the cause of the mysterious deaths until a French doctor, Caroline Stenger-Phillip, proposed a scientifically based explanation. When mummies were interred, treasures and other items, such as food, were placed in the tomb. King Tut's tomb contained fruits and vegetables, which grew mold. Mold spores, which contain bacteria, are released into the air. People who entered the tomb breathed these particles, and some may have had severe allergic reactions. It is now believed that Lord Carnarvon was already ill when he ventured to Egypt, and King Tut's tomb had nothing to do with his death. Although Stenger-Phillip's explanation steals a little excitement from the mystery of Tut's tomb and his mummy's curse, Howard Carter's find remains a truly amazing discovery that opened the window to a long-lost world.

QUESTIONS

1. **Which of the following would be the best title for this passage?**
   - **A.** King Tut's Curse
   - **B.** Mummies Are Our Friends
   - **C.** Mummies Are the Enemy
   - **D.** Mummies of Egypt

2. **What is the purpose of this passage?**
   - **A.** to prove that mummies are dangerous
   - **B.** to prove that legends are always false
   - **C.** to inform the reader about a famous legend
   - **D.** to inform the reader about how the media portray curses

3. **Which of the following best describes the reason for the first paragraph?**
   - **A.** It shows how ideas can change over time.
   - **B.** It proves that mummies have magical powers.
   - **C.** It explains why people are afraid of mummies.
   - **D.** It tells about King Tut's curse.

4. **As used in the passage, the word *revenge* most nearly means**
   - **A.** insult.
   - **B.** punishment.
   - **C.** freedom.
   - **D.** friendship.

5. **The legend of Tut's curse most likely**
   - **A.** attracted television reporters to the scene.
   - **B.** brought tourists to observe Carnarvon in action.
   - **C.** stirred up mold and spread illness.
   - **D.** discouraged people from looting ancient tombs.

6. ***Answer the following question using complete sentences:***
   Is the curse of King Tut fact or purely legend?

DIRECTIONS: *Read the passage and answer the questions that follow it.*

Gentle Giants

MANATEES, ALSO KNOWN AS sea cows, are large aquatic mammals that live in tropical coastal marshy areas. They live and feed in both salt and fresh water. Manatees are herbivores and eat ten to fifteen percent of their body weight in aquatic plants and other vegetation per day. They spend most of their time peacefully grazing, resting, body surfing, and traveling. The manatee has a large, streamlined, grayish-brown body with a flat, paddle-shaped tail and two flippers with fingernails. They have wrinkled faces with whiskers on their snouts. Their closest living relative is the elephant. The average adult, which can live more than sixty years, weighs upwards of 1000 pounds and grows to be approximately ten feet in length. Three species of manatee currently exist today: the West Indian, West African, and Amazonian. The Steller's sea cow was hunted to the point of extinction in 1768.

Some species of manatees are endangered, primarily because human activities have interfered with their habitat and food supply. Although the manatee's coastal areas have been reduced by expansion, this is not the only reason for their decline. The mammals are often injured by the propellers of motorboats while swimming through the waters. Fishing materials, such as fishing line and hooks, can clog or injure their digestive systems and cause death. Manatees are protected under federal law in the U.S. The Marine Mammal Protection Act of 1972 and the Endangered Species Act of 1973 declare it illegal to harass, hunt, capture, or kill any marine mammal. The Florida Manatee Recovery Plan of 1980 was developed to move the manatee onto the endangered species list. (Manatees in Florida were previously hunted for their oil and flesh.) Other measures have been taken to try to protect and conserve these gentle mammals, including researching their habitat, reducing the speeds of motor craft, educating the public, and creating **sanctuaries**. ○

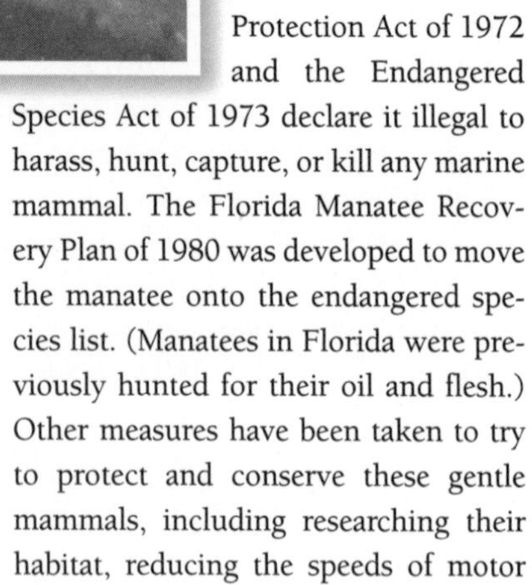

QUESTIONS

1. Which of the following best states the author's purpose?

- **A.** to inform the reader about aquatic animals who are endangered
- **B.** to inform the reader about an endangered aquatic mammal
- **C.** to describe the life of a manatee
- **D.** to describe important acts created to preserve endangered mammals

2. Which of the following is not an example of typical manatee behavior?

- **A.** grazing on vegetation
- **B.** body surfing
- **C.** hunting smaller fish for food
- **D.** resting between meals

3. Which of the following best describes the reason for the final paragraph?

- **A.** It informs the reader about important federal legislation to protect Manatees.
- **B.** It explains how the manatee became endangered and how it is being saved.
- **C.** It informs the reader about the best ways to help save manatees.
- **D.** It explains how dangerous human activities can be to marine life.

4. Which statement best describes the manatee?

- **A.** The manatee is a gentle marine mammal that spends most of its time eating.
- **B.** The manatee is a carnivorous marine mammal that lives in warm waters.
- **C.** The manatee is a herbivore that spends most of its time fleeing from predators.
- **D.** The manatee, which resembles the elephant, is an aquatic mammal.

5. Which statement best describes the manatee's status on the endangered species list?

- **A.** Manatees have been on the endangered species list since they became extinct in 1768.
- **B.** Manatees were placed on the endangered species list because they were hunted for their oil and flesh.
- **C.** Manatees have become endangered because of human interference in their lives.
- **D.** Manatees have become endangered because their young are easy prey for sharks.

6. As used in the passage, the word *sanctuaries* most nearly means

- **A.** protected shelters.
- **B.** theme parks.
- **C.** research facilities.
- **D.** open waters.

DIRECTIONS: *Read the passage and answer the questions that follow it.*

Motocross

MOTOCROSS IS CONSIDERED the most popular form of motorcycle racing. Riders race motorcycles or all terrain vehicles (ATV's) on enclosed off-road courses that often feature man-made jumps. The sport was invented in the United Kingdom and was called "scrambling." The name "motocross" is a combination of "motorcycle" and "cross country" and is abbreviated as "MX." Motocross can be broken down into specific categories, such as Supercross, Arenacross, Supermoto, and Freestyle. Both Supercross and Arenacross events are held indoors. Supermoto racers use motocross vehicles, but race on both off- and on-road courses. In Freestyle, or FMX, competitions, racers are judged by their ability to perform stunts while jumping through the air.

Motocross competitors ride special motorcycles that are lightweight and have engines geared for quick acceleration. The bikes have knobby tires to help grip the loose surfaces on the track. The bikes also have special features, such as banana-shaped seats and tough suspensions, to protect the rider during heavy landings. Motocross bikes can be purchased as ready-to-race from major motorcycle manufacturers; professional riders call these "factory bikes," but most professional riders prefer to modify their bikes to **enhance** performance and control.

Motocross races are segmented by laps or time periods. In lap races, a set number of laps is declared for the race, and the first racer to complete the laps is the winner. In timed races, participants take part in two or three sessions, called motos. After a rider competes in both, the scores are averaged together to produce an overall number. Professional motocross races, however, have their own format. During the race, after 30 minutes have passed, and the leader finishes the lap, a flag is waved to signal two more laps remain. The race is over once the winner crosses the finish line. In all motocross races, racers entertain viewers by doing amazing jumps and maintaining their balance while sliding, spinning tires, and making sharp turns. ⭘

QUESTIONS

1. Why did the author write this passage?

A. to get more people interested in motocross racing

B. to inform the reader about a popular sport

C. to explain how racers compete in motorcycle sports

D. to inform the reader about the dangers of motorcycle racing

2. Which of the following would be the best title for this passage?

A. MX Versus FMX

B. Racing Motorcycles

C. MX Racing

D. Racing Dangers

3. What is the author's attitude toward the sport?

A. The author does not reveal an opinion.

B. The author thinks motocross is a demanding sport.

C. The author is a motocross racer, who likes the sport.

D. The author believes motocross is a dangerous sport.

4. Why do professional motocross athletes alter their bikes?

A. They can make their bikes faster to increase their chances of winning.

B. They do not like factory bikes because of their weight.

C. It helps them feel more involved in their sport.

D. They can achieve better performance and more control.

5. As used in the passage, the word *enhance* most nearly means

A. decorate.

B. beautify.

C. improve.

D. quicken.

6. According to the passage, which statement is true?

A. Motocross racing was invented and named in the United States.

B. Motocross races occur in laps or time periods.

C. Freestyle racing is held indoors.

D. Racers compete on street motorcycles.

DIRECTIONS: *Read the passage and answer the questions that follow it.*

Elizabeth Cady Stanton

ELIZABETH CADY STANTON was a feminist who fought for women's suffrage. She was born in 1815, in Jamestown, New York, and married Henry B. Stanton, an abolitionist, in 1840, against her father's wishes. During their honeymoon in London, they visited the World's Antislavery Convention. Here, she met Lucretia Mott, America's leading female abolitionist. Soon thereafter, Elizabeth began to study women's rights.

Elizabeth Stanton was the mother of seven children, but soon began to **resent** her domestic life. In 1848, Stanton and Mott organized the first women's rights convention, which was held in Seneca Falls, New York. Stanton wanted one of the convention's goals to be voting rights for women. In 1851, Stanton met Susan B. Anthony, and they formed a lifelong partnership based on their desire to raise women's status. During the Civil War, Stanton and Anthony formed the National Women's League, an organization that fought to end slavery, using the Constitution as support for their claims.

After the war ended, the two women caused conflict when they tried to link the efforts of suffrage for women and African Americans. They were determined to use the Constitution as a means to secure voting; consequently, they established the National Woman Suffrage Association in 1869. Although this organization helped secure the Nineteenth Amendment, it was not ratified until 1920. Stanton was an advocate for divorce, believed in reproductive freedom, and wanted more freedom for women. Christian organizations opposed her agenda, and she found herself opposed to Susan B. Anthony. Although many disagreed with her ideas, she kept fighting for the causes she believed in, including suffrage, until she died in 1902.

QUESTIONS

1. **Which of the following would be the best title for this passage?**
   - **A.** Life of an Abolitionist
   - **B.** Unhappy Housewives
   - **C.** Fighting for Suffrage
   - **D.** Using the Constitution

2. **Which of the following best states the author's purpose?**
   - **A.** to describe how rights for women and African Americans were fought together
   - **B.** to show how women can fight against society
   - **C.** to describe how one woman helped obtain rights for all women
   - **D.** to describe how slavery was abolished and suffrage was obtained

3. **Which best describes the reason for the last paragraph?**
   - **A.** It tells how Stanton fought for her causes, no matter who opposed her.
   - **B.** It describes the role of the National Woman Suffrage Association.
   - **C.** It explains how much influence religious organizations have on society.
   - **D.** It explains how women used the Constitution to secure suffrage.

4. **Why did Elizabeth Stanton fight?**
   - **A.** Stanton fought for causes with the help of religious sponsorship.
   - **B.** Stanton fought for causes that liberated women.
   - **C.** Stanton fought for constitutional amendments to keep slavery legal.
   - **D.** Stanton fought for abolishing divorce laws.

5. **As used in the passage, the word *resent* most nearly means feeling**
   - **A.** hopeful.
   - **B.** happy.
   - **C.** bitter.
   - **D.** isolated.

6. **According to the passage, when did Stanton become interested in feminism?**
   - **A.** after she went against her father's wishes about marriage
   - **B.** when she met Susan B. Anthony
   - **C.** after she had her children
   - **D.** after she met Lucretia Mott

DIRECTIONS: *Read the passage and answer the questions that follow it.*

Tasmanian Devils

THE TASMANIAN DEVIL is not an obnoxious, destructive cartoon character, but rather a marsupial, or pouched mammal, that lives only on the Australian island of Tasmania. Devils are nocturnal animals that inhabit the land between the coast and the mountains where they can find shelter during the day and food at night. Early European settlers called the animal the Devil because of its bad temper, its loud, chilling screeches, and the foul odor it emits when stressed. The devil uses coughs and sneezes as signals. A sharp sneeze is used to challenge another devil to fight, while screeches are used to show aggression during feeding. The devil has a thick, muscular build and is about the size of a small dog. The devil's fur is predominantly black, and it has a short, stubby tail. Long whiskers on the devil's face and head help it locate prey in the dark and sense the closeness of others while feeding. The devil is the largest **carnivorous** marsupial in the world and is incredibly vicious when feeding on whatever it finds. The jaws of a devil are very powerful; in fact, they have the strongest bite of any living mammal. Their jaws and teeth let them eat all parts of prey, including bones and fur, and because they clean carcasses, they help reduce the risk of diseases to livestock.

During pregnancy, devils gestate for twenty to thirty days. The female usually gives birth to more young than can fit in her pouch, where the survivors mature for approximately four months. Then, they venture out on their own. Tasmanian devil young are weaned at around five or six months, and then they leave their mother. The average Tasmanian devil's life span is six years.

Tasmanian devils have endured numerous challenges to their survival. In the 1300s, they became extinct on the Australian mainland. On Tasmania, they had been considered a threat to livestock and hunted to near extinction, but they became a protected species in 1941. Their numbers are also challenged by a tumor disease, and they may soon be added to the endangered species list. ⭘

QUESTIONS

1. **According to the passage, Tasmanian devils are nearing extinction because**
   - **A.** they have been hunted for their fur and tusks.
   - **B.** they have been hunted because they pose a threat to livestock.
   - **C.** they live on only one island and are exhausting their food supply.
   - **D.** they cannot escape their predators.

2. **Which of the following would be the best title for this passage?**
   - **A.** The Australian Devil
   - **B.** Vicious Marsupials
   - **C.** The Tasmanian Devil, Dracula's Cousin
   - **D.** The Carnivorous Devil

3. **Which of the following best describes the reason for the final paragraph?**
   - **A.** It informs the reader about the devil's threats to farmers and livestock.
   - **B.** It describes devil's facial tumor disease.
   - **C.** It tells the reader why the devil may become endangered.
   - **D.** It explains why the devil became protected.

4. **Which statement best describes the Tasmanian devil?**
   - **A.** The devil is a small, nocturnal carnivore.
   - **B.** The devil is a large, carnivorous marsupial.
   - **C.** The devil is a nocturnal herbivore.
   - **D.** The devil is small herbivore.

5. **As used in the passage, the word *carnivorous* most nearly means**
   - **A.** noise-making.
   - **B.** meat-eating.
   - **C.** plant-eating.
   - **D.** insect-eating.

6. **According to the passage, which statement is true?**
   - **A.** The female devil gives birth after being pregnant for five months.
   - **B.** The devil gives off a foul odor when it is content.
   - **C.** The devil became extinct from Australia's mainland after European settlers arrived.
   - **D.** The devil became protected in 1941.

DIRECTIONS: *Read the passage and answer the questions that follow it.*

Gold, Greed, and Grief

IN 1848, A MONUMENTAL DISCOVERY in California changed the course of American history and defined a generation of pioneers. As Sutter's Mill was under construction, laborers there found gold. This discovery inspired a mass migration west in hopes of finding fortune. The Gold Rush is sometimes considered a period during which many people were rewarded with riches for their hard work. Those already living in the areas affected by the rush, however, were not as fortunate. To Native American tribes, the Gold Rush was a powerful force that all but destroyed their way of life.

At the time of the discovery, the land in California belonged to Mexico and was occupied by the Mewuk and Maidu tribes. Nonetheless, the governor of Mexico granted John Sutter 48,000 acres. The Native Americans completed most of the work on the Sutter Ranch, but not willingly. One reportedly testified, "My grandfather was enslaved by Sutter to help in building the Fort. While he was kept there, Sutter worked him hard and then fed him in troughs. As soon as he could, he escaped with his family and hid in the mountains."

Native Americans who were not working at Sutter's Ranch faced even greater cruelty. Beginning the summer after the gold discovery, in an effort to secure the land for the pioneers, the California legislature created laws and adopted policies that essentially became **genocide**. Soon, bounty hunters were awarded money in return for proof that they had killed Native Americans, and massacre campaigns were led to wipe out entire villages. The Act for the Government and Protection of Indians (1850) allowed white settlers to force the original inhabitants to work for them. These laws were abused to permit kidnapping, slavery, and murder of Native Americans, resulting in the enslavement of countless people, particularly women and children. In 1853, the U.S. Senate started making treaties with the tribes to acquire their land. However, the treaties were never ratified, and Native Americans were forced onto reservations where they did not have ample fertile ground and game to ensure their survival. While many tried to resist the government and protect their way of life, thousands ultimately lost their lives and their traditional land.

QUESTIONS

1. **Why did the government pass laws that harmed Native Americans?**
   - **A.** The pioneers were afraid of the Mewuk and Maidu Indians.
   - **B.** The Native Americans lived on the land that the pioneers wanted.
   - **C.** The pioneers needed the Native Americans to help them build forts and mills.
   - **D.** The Native Americans threatened the pioneers.

2. **Which of the following best states the author's purpose?**
   - **A.** to explain why many people went to California in the mid 1800s
   - **B.** to show how the government passed legislation during the Gold Rush
   - **C.** to describe how the Gold Rush affected Native Americans
   - **D.** to explain how Native Americans were forced into slavery

3. **Which of the following best describes the reason for the final paragraph?**
   - **A.** It describes some of the legislation the government enacted against Native Americans.
   - **B.** It explains how Native Americans were treated on Sutter Ranch.
   - **C.** It describes how the practice of scalping began.
   - **D.** It explains how California tried to protect Native Americans from white settlers.

4. **Which statement best describes the effects of the government's attitude towards the Native Americans?**
   - **A.** Settlers and Native Americans began to live side by side.
   - **B.** Indians who acted violently toward settlers were punished.
   - **C.** Indians moved to different lands where they lived peacefully.
   - **D.** The Native American populations diminished, and they lost their land.

5. **As used in the passage, the word *genocide* most nearly means**
   - **A.** extermination.
   - **B.** thievery.
   - **C.** negotiation.
   - **D.** preparation.

6. ***Answer the following question using complete sentences:***
   What can be inferred about the situation at the Sutter Ranch by the quote dealing with one man's grandfather?

DIRECTIONS: *Read the passage and answer the questions that follow it.*

Maya Angelou

MAYA ANGELOU WAS BORN on April 4, 1928, in St. Louis, Missouri, as Marguerite Annie Johnson. She is well known for her works as an author, poet, and civil rights activist. Her most famous autobiographical book, *I Know Why the Caged Bird Sings,* was nominated for the National Book Award. One volume of her poetry, *Just Give Me a Cool Drink of Water 'fore I Diiie* (1971), was nominated for the Pulitzer Prize. While most people know her for her literary work, she also participated in more dramatic art forms. She was the first black female director in Hollywood. She wrote, produced, directed, and starred in films, television shows, and stage productions. Her performance in the TV miniseries of *Roots* showed her acting ability, and her Broadway debut in *Look Away* earned her a nomination for a Tony award.

In 1959, Maya Angelou became the northern coordinator for the Southern Christian Leadership Conference at the request of Dr. Martin Luther King, Jr., the founder of the group. This organization believed in using nonviolent resistance to get equal rights for African Americans. During the 1960s, Angelou lived in parts of Africa working as a journalist and a teacher. After returning to the U.S. in 1974, she taught at leading universities and received many honorary degrees. She also served on boards of several **prestigious** arts and civics organizations. Furthermore, President Bill Clinton asked her to recite a poem for his first inauguration in 1993. For that day, she wrote "On the Pulse of Morning." This poem, along with much of her work, is now celebrated and honored. Angelou has received many awards, including the Presidential Medal of Freedom, the highest United States civilian award, which was bestowed upon her by President Obama in 2011.

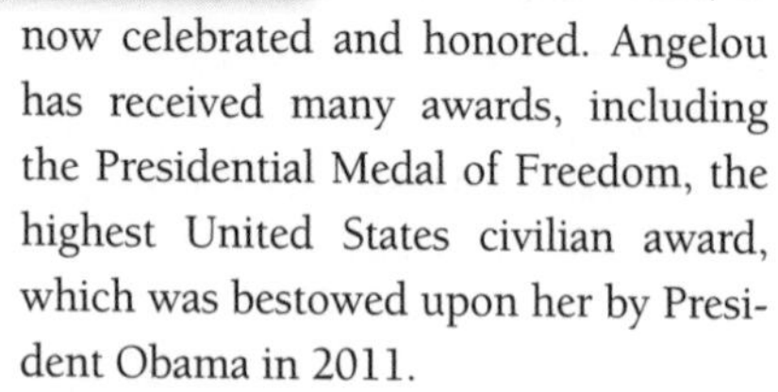

Maya Angelou died in 2014, while working on an additional volume of her autobiography, dealing with many of the famous political leaders she had known. She will be remembered for her amazing body of work, including essays, poems, plays, and seven autobiographies that cover various portions of her life.

QUESTIONS

1. **Which of the following is the best title for this passage?**
   - **A.** Maya Angelou's Awards
   - **B.** The Life of Maya Angelou
   - **C.** Maya and the American Dream
   - **D.** Maya's Magic with Words

2. **Which of the following best states the author's purpose?**
   - **A.** to show Maya Angelou's influence on society in the mid-1900s
   - **B.** to highlight some of the awards Maya Angelou received
   - **C.** to explain why so many people like Ms. Angelou
   - **D.** to inform the reader about an influential artist

3. **Why does the author mention Angelou's role in politics?**
   - **A.** to describe Angelou's social worries
   - **B.** to show that Angelou and King were friends
   - **C.** to explain why Angelou traveled to Africa
   - **D.** to show Angelou's importance

4. **As used in the passage, the word *prestigious* most nearly means**
   - **A.** prejudiced.
   - **B.** active.
   - **C.** respected.
   - **D.** political.

5. **According to the passage, which statement about Maya Angelou is true?**
   - **A.** Angelou was a respected literary author who worked only in education.
   - **B.** Angelou's literary work is often promoted by former U.S. presidents.
   - **C.** Angelou is known for her literary work and social and political efforts.
   - **D.** Angelou worked with King on violent campaigns to get equal rights for African Americans.

6. ***Answer the following question using complete sentences:***
   What message did Maya Angelou teach through her activities and art?

DIRECTIONS: *Read the passage and answer the questions that follow it.*

Forks and Knives Go Hand-in-Hand

PEOPLE HAVE NOT ALWAYS used forks to eat their food. In fact, it was not until the late 1800s, during the Industrial Revolution, that owning and using a complete set of matching utensils became common for all classes. Before this utensil became **prevalent** at the table, people mainly used knives and spoons to eat. However, most eating was done with the hands. The Romans used forks, which had only two straight tines, for serving food.

A Byzantine princess brought forks to Italy in the 11th century when she married the Doge of Venice. During a party in her honor, she refused to eat with her hands. Instead, a servant cut her food, and she ate it with a golden fork. The people of Venice ridiculed her for using such an instrument. Many religious leaders considered the fork an "excessive delicacy" and disapproved of its use. It was not until the 16th century that using a fork became common and acceptable in Italy. An Englishman named Thomas Coryate brought forks to England after seeing them in Italy in 1608. The English called the forks unnecessary. "Why should a person need a fork when he has hands?" they questioned. However, forks, which were made of precious metals and were often encrusted with jewels, were soon being used by the wealthy in England, France, and throughout Europe.

In the 17th century, more tines were added to the fork, and manufacturers started curving the tines so people could scoop food. Since the fork made spearing food with a knife unnecessary, knives were soon made with rounded tips. In an attempt to stop violence, King Louis XIV of France even declared pointed knives illegal. No one could carry or use a pointed knife for any purpose. The French quickly obeyed the law and had the tips of all their existing knives ground. This new style soon spread throughout England and Europe. By the 19th century, all classes were using forks and rounded knives regularly.

QUESTIONS

1. **Which of the following best states the author's purpose?**
   - **A.** to inform the reader about different types of utensils
   - **B.** to describe how people started using forks
   - **C.** to explain how forks were first manufactured
   - **D.** to describe why using a fork was unpopular in the past

2. **Why did people have a hard time accepting the fork?**
   - **A.** The fork looked foreign and strange.
   - **B.** Religious leaders told people not to use forks.
   - **C.** Forks were fancy and encrusted with jewels.
   - **D.** People had never before used forks to eat.

3. **Which of the following statements best describes the reason for the second paragraph?**
   - **A.** It describes how leaders viewed the use of utensils.
   - **B.** It explains how the fork became popular in France.
   - **C.** It explains how some critics viewed the fork as unnecessary or immoral.
   - **D.** It proves that only the wealthy used utensils.

4. **According to the passage, which statement best describes the fork's history?**
   - **A.** Forks were previously designed with only two straight tines; the design did not change until the 17th century.
   - **B.** Forks were declared illegal in France; this prevented the utensil from becoming popular until the Industrial Revolution.
   - **C.** Forks originated in Italy during the 17th century; their use quickly spread throughout Europe.
   - **D.** Forks have been commonly used since Roman times for serving and eating.

5. **As used in the passage, the word *prevalent* most nearly means**
   - **A.** rare.
   - **B.** legal.
   - **C.** used.
   - **D.** common.

6. **According to the passage, which statement is true?**
   - **A.** The fork's usefulness led to design changes in knives.
   - **B.** Forks were poorly designed and were useful only for serving meat.
   - **C.** A Byzantine princess spoke against using forks in Italy.
   - **D.** Forks became popular in upper classes after lower classes started using them regularly.

DIRECTIONS: *Read the passage and answer the questions that follow it.*

The Great Wall of China

THE GREAT WALL OF CHINA is perhaps one of the most spectacular examples of ancient **engineering**. Standing approximately twenty-five feet tall and stretching 1,500 miles across Northern China, the Wall has been called one of the "Seven Medieval Wonders of the World." The Wall, which is lined with watchtowers, was built to protect northern China from invaders, but was ineffective.

Construction of the Wall began sometime around 700 B.C., and continued for two thousand years. The Great Wall started as many separate walls that were built by different rulers. Emperor Qin Shi Huang, however, ordered the walls to be joined in 214 B.C. Laborers used local materials to build and connect the walls. Before the use of bricks, the Wall was made of dirt, stones, and wood. The walls were usually filled with packed earth and rubble. In areas near the mountains, rocks were taken and used for construction. Desert regions, however, used only dirt and wood. During the peak of the construction, there were 1.8 million laborers working on it. Many of the workers were criminals, soldiers, or slaves. The physical demands of building such a structure were incredible. So many people died during the construction of the Great Wall that it has been called "the longest cemetery on Earth," or "the long graveyard."

Unfortunately, much of the Wall is now in disrepair. People have used the stones to repair other structures, children use crumbling segments as playgrounds, and some sections have been destroyed by new construction. It is estimated that only twenty percent of the Wall remains in good condition. Most of these sections were built using longer-lasting materials during the Ming Dynasty in the seventeenth century. Despite the damage it has suffered, the Great Wall of China remains a major tourist attraction and a monument to the amazing efforts of the countless numbers who built it.

QUESTIONS

1. Which of the following would be the best title for this passage?

- **A.** The Great Chinese Construction
- **B.** China's Amazing Monument
- **C.** The Great Wall: Keeping Enemies Out
- **D.** The Great Wall: A Lingering Achievement

2. Why do you think the author wrote this passage?

- **A.** to show the importance of the Great Wall of China
- **B.** to inform the reader about ancient construction methods
- **C.** to explain how the Great Wall got its name
- **D.** to explain how and why the Wall was built

3. Which of the following best describes the reason for the last paragraph?

- **A.** It names the most important Chinese dynasty.
- **B.** It explains the current state of the Great Wall.
- **C.** It explains why the Wall was built.
- **D.** It proves that good construction materials are important if a structure is to last.

4. Why was the Great Wall of China built?

- **A.** The Wall was built as a monument to the Emperor.
- **B.** The Wall was built as a tourist attraction.
- **C.** The Wall was built for protection from outsiders.
- **D.** The Wall was built to keep citizens from escaping.

5. As used in the passage, the word *engineering* most nearly means

- **A.** technology.
- **B.** science.
- **C.** mathematics.
- **D.** methods.

6. Which of the following best describes the methods of constructing the Great Wall?

- **A.** Criminals and slaves were buried along the Wall.
- **B.** The Wall was constructed with local materials, such as earth and stone.
- **C.** The Wall was constructed with stones and cement.
- **D.** Existing walls were joined together by local construction workers.

DIRECTIONS: *Read the passage and answer the questions that follow it.*

Harriet Tubman: The Moses of Her People

HARRIET TUBMAN WAS FAMOUS for her efforts with the Underground Railroad, a secret network developed to help slaves escape to Canada. Born into slavery some time between 1819 and 1822, as Araminta Ross, Tubman was the fifth of nine children. By the time Harriet was six years old, her owner, Edward Brodess, made a frequent practice of hiring her to other slave masters, many of whom were cruel to her. One master threw a weight at her and struck her head. The blow caused permanent damage, which resulted in periodic epileptic seizures that she would experience for the rest of her life. As an adult, Harriet took her mother's name and married John Tubman, a freed slave, in 1844.

Brodess died in 1849, leaving his wife to support eight children. To pay the debts, Mrs. Brodess sold members of Harriet Tubman's family. Fearing being sold into the Deep South, Tubman fled north to Philadelphia, leaving her family behind. For the next ten years, Tubman returned to the South more than a dozen times helping slaves escape via the Underground Railroad. Called "the Moses of her people," Harriet helped more than 300 slaves, including her parents and four brothers, escape. Tubman never lost a fugitive and never allowed one to retreat to slavery. She kept a loaded revolver at her side to defend herself against the bounty hunters who searched for her, and also to keep slaves from having second thoughts and turning back. She also armed herself with her faith and relied heavily on God for strength and protection.

Tubman continued to fight against slavery during the Civil War while working as a nurse, cook, scout, and spy for the North. In 1863, she led a raid in South Carolina that allowed more than 700 slaves to escape onto Union ships. This was the first military operation in U.S. history planned and executed by a woman. While she played an active role in the military, she was not paid until thirty years later for her services. After the war, Tubman moved to New York and married Nelson Davis, who was twenty-two years her junior. They lived in a home Tubman purchased and was used to care for aged and **indigent** freed slaves. ⭘

QUESTIONS

1. Which of the following best states the author's purpose?

A. to describe the Underground Railroad
B. to inform the reader about slavery and abolitionists
C. to describe a famous female abolitionist
D. to inform the reader about the Civil War

2. Which of the following can you infer was Tubman's strongest quality?

A. intelligence
B. friendliness
C. determination
D. humor

3. Which best describes the reason for the first paragraph?

A. It describes Tubman's life as a slave.
B. It explains the cruelty many slaves endured at the hands of masters.
C. It explains the origin of Tubman's name.
D. It describes how Edward Brodess treated her.

4. Which statement best describes the life of Harriet Tubman?

A. Tubman was a brave woman who always stuck by her family.
B. Tubman spent her life trying to help fellow slaves escape.
C. Tubman was a white female abolitionist.
D. Tubman was a spy during the Civil War.

5. As used in the passage, the word *indigent* most nearly means

A. educated.
B. dying.
C. rich.
D. impoverished.

6. According to the passage, which of the following statements is true?

A. Tubman was the first woman in U.S. military history to lead a raid.
B. Tubman used her pistol to shoot slaves who would not board the Underground Railroad.
C. Tubman was not a Christian woman.
D. Tubman was a spy against the Union Army.

DIRECTIONS: *Read the passage and answer the questions that follow it.*

Hatshepsut

HATSHEPSUT IS ONE OF the earliest known reigning queens in history. Having lived during the late fifteenth century B.C., in Egypt, Hatshepsut is only the third female known to have taken the male title of Pharaoh. When her father, Thutmose I, died in 1492 BC, she married her half-brother, Thutmose II. Although Thutmose II ruled for thirteen years, Hatshepsut had a strong influence over him. When Thutmose II died, Thutmose III, Hatshepsut's stepson, was the next to receive the throne. Because he was not yet of age, Hatshepsut ruled for him. Before he was old enough to assume the reign, however, Hatshepsut was herself crowned Pharaoh and ruled in her own right. As Pharaoh, she wore the traditional **regalia**, such as the head cloth, kilt, and even a chin beard. She is portrayed as a male in many of the statues and images she had constructed.

Hatshepsut is known as a "builder Pharaoh" since she commissioned hundreds of construction projects throughout Egypt. So many statues were produced during her time that every major museum in the world currently has an object from her reign on display. While her twenty-two-year reign was marked as a peaceful time, there is evidence that she led military campaigns in Nubia, Levant, and Syria. She was also able to rebuild Egypt's trade networks and increase the country's wealth.

Hatshepsut died in 1458 B.C. She was middle aged at that time. While no record of the cause of her death survives, researchers theorize it was from natural causes. After her death, Thutmose III tried to erase her reign by ordering the destruction of her monuments and removing her face from carved images. Exactly why he tried remains unknown, but he was quite effective, as historians knew nothing about her until 1903, when archaeologist Howard Carter discovered her tomb and her story.

QUESTIONS

1. **Which of the following would be the best title for this passage?**
   - **A.** Female Pharaohs of Egypt
   - **B.** Hatshepsut: the Forgotten Female Pharaoh
   - **C.** Builder Pharaohs and Female Leaders
   - **D.** Egyptian Family Battles, B.C.

2. **Which of the following best states the author's purpose?**
   - **A.** to show the power of women in ancient Egypt
   - **B.** to explain how Hatshepsut came to power
   - **C.** to describe the reign of a female pharaoh
   - **D.** to explain why Hatshepsut married Thutmose II

3. **As used in the passage, the word *regalia* most nearly means**
   - **A.** crowns.
   - **B.** tools.
   - **C.** clothing.
   - **D.** symbols.

4. **How did historians learn about Hatshepsut?**
   - **A.** Her stepson was unable to erase the memory of her reign.
   - **B.** Her story was revealed in her tomb.
   - **C.** Assistants to the pharaoh recorded details about her reign.
   - **D.** The statues she commissioned told her story.

5. **Which statement best describes Hatshepsut?**
   - **A.** She was a builder pharaoh who also focused on trade.
   - **B.** She was a self-absorbed builder pharaoh.
   - **C.** She was the last female pharaoh to rule in her own right.
   - **D.** She was a pharaoh who refused to dress as a male.

6. ***Answer the following question using complete sentences:***
   Why might Thutmose III have tried to erase Hatshepsut from history?

DIRECTIONS: *Read the passage and answer the questions that follow it.*

6LL3

DOLLY, A FEMALE SHEEP, was the first mammal to be cloned from adult cells. Dolly, who was cloned at the Roslin Institute in Scotland, was born on July 5, 1996. The scientists, under the leadership of Ian Wilmut, created her by taking the cells from the udder of a pregnant six-year-old sheep and inserting them into the uterus of another sheep to develop. As a clone, Dolly was an exact **replica** of the pregnant six-year-old sheep. Her original name was "6LL3," but she was nicknamed Dolly in honor of Dolly Parton, a famous actress and country-western singer.

Dolly the sheep lived to be only six years old, which is half the lifespan of a normal sheep. At the age of five, Dolly showed early signs of arthritis. Some researchers think she could have been prone to premature aging because she was a clone, but others doubt that. In 2003, Dolly was euthanized because she developed incurable lung disease. That April, her stuffed remains were put on exhibit at Edinburgh's Royal Museum in Scotland.

Dolly's short life span has caused controversy among many scientists and researchers. Those in favor of cloning animals argue that endangered species could be preserved, and clones could be used for many research purposes to benefit humans and cure diseases. However, because not all effects of cloning are known, many think that cloning is wrong, especially when it involves humans. Some people are so opposed to cloning that they believe it should be banned. The debate still rages, and Dolly and the practice of cloning will continue to be a topic of controversy for many years.

QUESTIONS

1. **Which of the following best states the author's purpose?**
   A. to inform the reader about the controversies surrounding cloning
   B. to explain why cloning is dangerous
   C. to inform the reader about a cloned sheep
   D. to describe how cloning is done

2. **How does the author feel about cloning?**
   A. The author does not reveal his or her feelings.
   B. The author feels that cloning is risky.
   C. The author thinks cloning is beneficial to humans.
   D. The author feels that cloning is the only way to cure diseases.

3. **What is the purpose of the first paragraph?**
   A. It describes how Dolly lived after being cloned.
   B. It describes how Dolly was cloned.
   C. It mentions Dolly's birthplace and creators.
   D. It explains the significance of DNA in cloning.

4. **According to the passage, how was Dolly created?**
   A. Cells from Dolly's mother were put into an already pregnant sheep.
   B. Cells from an udder were put into a pregnant sheep.
   C. Cells from a pregnant sheep were put into another sheep.
   D. Cells from a six-year-old sheep were put into a pregnant sheep.

5. **As used in the passage, the word *replica* most nearly means:**
   A. daughter.
   B. ancestor.
   C. original.
   D. copy.

6. ***Answer the following question using complete sentences:***
   Why might some people disapprove of the practice of cloning animals and humans?

DIRECTIONS: *Read the passage and answer the questions that follow it.*

Hollow Earth

IN 1692, AN ENGLISH ASTRONOMER named Edmund Halley, who discovered the comet that bears his name, proposed an interesting theory about the center of the earth. Halley believed that the center of the earth was actually hollow and able to **sustain** life. After studying the earth, he claimed there were four different magnetic fields. These fields were actually spheres layered inside each other within the planet. He also theorized that the very center of the earth contained life and was lit by a luminous atmosphere. According to this theory, the lights at the North Pole, called "aurora borealis," are caused by the core atmosphere's gasses escaping through a hole.

Halley was not the only one to believe in this hollow-Earth theory. Many other scientists agreed with Halley and added their own interpretations. A Swiss mathematician named Leonard Euler claimed that the core of the earth was a single hollow sphere where an advanced civilization resided. The civilization received heat and light from a 600-mile-wide sun that existed inside the core.

Although many supporters believed Halley's theory, the most passionate may have been John Symmes, who believed that the earth was hollow and that the North and South Poles were entranceways 4,000 to 6,000 miles wide into the core. Symmes, while dedicating his life to advancing his theory, spent much of his time raising money to fund expeditions to the North Pole to explore the inner earth. Although he was not successful, the U.S. government funded an expedition to Antarctica in 1838. Explorers did not find Symmes's hole, but they did realize Antarctica was, in fact, a continent.

In 1926, Navy Admiral Richard Byrd flew across the North Pole and reported no holes leading to inner-Earth. There is also no evidence in photographs taken by astronauts, either. However, this lack of evidence does not stop some people today from believing in the hollow-Earth theory. They argue that the holes exist, and at least one travel agency offers a hollow-Earth expedition costing tens of thousands of dollars, which, depending on the weather and the amount of ice, may or may not even reach the pole.

QUESTIONS

1. Which of the following best states the author's purpose?

- **A.** to prove that the earth is hollow
- **B.** to explain Edmund Halley's ideas about our planet
- **C.** to inform the reader about hollow-Earth theories
- **D.** to explain different theories about the earth

2. Which of the following would be the best title for this passage?

- **A.** Theories about the Earth's Core
- **B.** Aliens Living in Earth's Core
- **C.** Living in the Earth's Core
- **D.** Expeditions to Inner Earth

3. What is the purpose of the second paragraph?

- **A.** It explains the type of civilization that lives inside the earth's core.
- **B.** It informs the reader about another theorist's ideas on the subject.
- **C.** It describes the core of the earth according to Halley's own ideas.
- **D.** It tells the reader how to enter the earth's core.

4. According to the passage, how did Halley come up with his theory?

- **A.** Halley came up with his theory after studying the aurora borealis.
- **B.** Halley came up with his theory after leading an expedition to the North Pole.
- **C.** Halley came up with his theory after studying the earth's magnetic fields.
- **D.** Halley came up with his theory after discovering Halley's comet, which is named after him.

5. As used in the passage, the word *sustain* most nearly means

- **A.** support.
- **B.** prove.
- **C.** house.
- **D.** accept.

6. Why does the last paragraph mention the travel agency's expensive expedition?

- **A.** It proves that the photographic evidence is false.
- **B.** It demonstrates how the government tries to disprove theories with which it disagrees.
- **C.** It demonstrates how strongly some people believe in the hollow-Earth theory.
- **D.** It informs the reader about John Symmes, the originator of the hollow-Earth theory.

DIRECTIONS: *Read the passage and answer the questions that follow it.*

Shrunken Heads

THE JIVARO PEOPLE REMOVED and shrank the heads of their enemies. These heads, called tsantsa, were kept as trophies and held spiritual significance. These people, who still live in remote parts of the rainforest in Peru and Ecuador, believed in the continuation of the spirit after death. Following a belief similar to that of wergild—the Anglo-Saxon code that asserted a clan was due payment, either in the form of wealth or the life of the enemy, when the enemy had killed one of the clan's members—the Jivaro would kill and decapitate an enemy who had killed one of their own members. Once they had carried out this vengeance for the death of their tribesman, the Jivaro would shrink the enemy's head to achieve several spiritual purposes. The Jivaro believed that their deceased relatives needed to be honored by the vengeful death of the enemy. They also believed that if they shrank the enemy's head, they effectively trapped his spirit so that it can harm neither the deceased relative nor the living tribesmen. Although the heads served a religious purpose, they were also seen as trophies and served as warnings to enemies. After the celebration of such an accomplishment, however, many of the tsantsa were simply discarded.

Making a tsantsa required an **elaborate** ritual. Once an enemy had been killed, the victors would carry his head back to camp. The head was then prepared: first, the hunters removed the skin from the skull by slicing from the top of the head to the neck. Then, they disposed of the skull and stitched closed the eyelids and lips. Next, the head was boiled in a pot with special herbs and tanners before being molded, stuffed, and sewn shut. Sometimes, the head would then be decorated with beads. Once complete, the tsantsa looked very similar to the original head, but was one-third the size. The hunters would then celebrate and show off the trophy to other tribe members and warriors in a victory feast called "la fiesta de victoria."

The Jivaro did not perform these rituals frequently and no longer do. However, in the past, collectors and tourists created a demand for tsantsa, and killings increased to make profits. The Peruvian and Ecuadoran governments outlawed selling the heads, but some collectors have managed to purchase them for thousands of dollars. Today, replicas of shrunken heads, which are made from leather, can be purchased easily.

QUESTIONS

1. **Why does the author explain "wergild" in the passage?**
   - **A.** to expose barbaric rituals of ancient people
   - **B.** to show how this belief is common to other cultures
   - **C.** to build credibility by adding details
   - **D.** to describe "la fiesta de victoria"

2. **Which of the following would be the best title for this passage?**
   - **A.** What is a Tsantsa
   - **B.** The Trade of Shrunken Heads
   - **C.** The Jivaro Tribe
   - **D.** Rainforest Headhunters

3. **What is the main purpose of the last paragraph?**
   - **A.** It describes the reasons tsantsa were first made.
   - **B.** It explains how the government interferes with native tribes.
   - **C.** It discusses the increase in trade of shrunken heads.
   - **D.** It informs the reader about tsantsa replicas.

4. **Which statement best describes the process of making tsantsa?**
   - **A.** The flesh is removed from the skull and boiled. Then, it is molded and stuffed.
   - **B.** The flesh is removed from the skull, stuffed, and sewn shut. Then, it is boiled and left to dry.
   - **C.** The skull is boiled in special herbs. Then, the flesh is removed from the skull, stuffed, and sewn shut.
   - **D.** The flesh is removed from the skull, molded, and sewn shut.

5. **As used in the passage, the word *elaborate* most nearly means**
   - **A.** speedy.
   - **B.** fancy.
   - **C.** gory.
   - **D.** complex.

6. ***Answer the following question using complete sentences:***
   Why did the Jivaro people make shrunken heads?

DIRECTIONS: *Read the passage and answer the questions that follow it.*

The Cure

Obesity is defined as weighing more than twenty percent over what is considered normal (according to age, height, and weight tables). Currently, between thirty and thirty-five percent of the U.S. population is overweight or obese. According to the Center for Disease Control and Prevention and the World Health Organization, this weight problem has become an epidemic in both the United States and the rest of the global community.

In the recent past, advertising and social norms have influenced people to view thinness as the ideal body type, but this skin-and-bones standard is unhealthy, both emotionally and physically. Currently, the medical community has become increasingly involved in promoting an awareness of healthy eating and exercise habits. The major problem with obesity, aside from the prejudices that often accompany it, is that being overweight **predisposes** a person to future serious health disorders, such as diabetes, high blood pressure, stroke, and heart disease. Being overweight has also been linked to an increased risk of colon, breast, and other cancers.

A person becomes overweight when he or she consumes more calories than what the body uses for energy. Insufficient exercise and overeating make this problem worse. Many people use food as a means of relieving boredom or for comfort during times of stress, both of which can lead to overeating. Currently, there is a debate about whether being overweight is the result of genetics or lifestyle. Several surgical treatments for weight loss have been developed over the years, including the drastic method of wiring the jaw shut and stapling or removing parts of the stomach to limit how much food can be consumed. Because the best practice is to cut calories and increase exercise, many people who are willing to undergo risky surgery fail to achieve long-term success. True success in achieving a healthy weight comes from living a healthy lifestyle and making healthy choices about food and exercise.

QUESTIONS

1. **Which sentence from the second paragraph needs to be followed by an explanation?**
   - **A.** In the recent past, advertising and social norms have influenced people to view thinness as the ideal body type, but this skin-and-bones standard is unhealthy, both emotionally and physically.
   - **B.** Currently, the medical community has become increasingly involved in promoting an awareness of healthy eating and healthy exercise habits.
   - **C.** The major problem with obesity, aside from the prejudices that often accompany it, is that being overweight predisposes a person to future serious health disorders, such as diabetes, high blood pressure, stroke, and heart disease.
   - **D.** Being overweight has also been linked to an increased risk of colon, breast, and other cancers.

2. **Why would the author have written this passage?**
   - **A.** to show how people can gain or lose weight
   - **B.** to show the causes and consequences of being overweight
   - **C.** to inform the reader about the lives of obese people
   - **D.** to explain why so many people in the U.S. are overweight

3. **Which of the following is the most logical conclusion from the passage?**
   - **A.** People can take drastic measures to lose weight.
   - **B.** People suffer from obesity as the result of unclear advertising messages.
   - **C.** People can best fight obesity with healthy food and exercise choices.
   - **D.** People suffer from obesity because of their genetic makeup.

4. **According to the passage, how do people become overweight?**
   - **A.** People become overweight when the body stores more calories than it burns.
   - **B.** People become overweight because of genetic disorders.
   - **C.** People become overweight when the body burns more calories than it consumes.
   - **D.** People become overweight because of other health conditions.

5. **According to the passage, what are the consequences of being overweight?**
   - **A.** People who are overweight face social stigma.
   - **B.** People who are overweight face discrimination.
   - **C.** People who are overweight risk serious health problems.
   - **D.** People who are overweight face stigma and are at risk for diseases.

6. **As used in the passage, the word *predisposes* most nearly means**
   - **A.** leads.
   - **B.** guarantees.
   - **C.** faces.
   - **D.** eliminates.

DIRECTIONS: *Read the passage and answer the questions that follow it.*

Icebergs

GIANT MASSES OF ICE afloat in the ocean, otherwise known as icebergs, are actually segments that have broken off a larger piece of ice, such as an ice sheet or snow-formed glacier. Approximately 90% of an iceberg is underwater, and its size and shape are hard to distinguish from the surface, which makes icebergs hazardous to ships. Icebergs are classified by their shape: rounded, irregular, or tabular. Rounded bergs are chunks of ice that have flipped, exposing their smoothed undersides. The type of iceberg that most people picture is the irregular iceberg, which means it has shape that is uneven—steep, jagged, conical. Tabular bergs are large and flat.

Most icebergs in the Atlantic Ocean originate from Greenland. In fact, the RMS *Titanic* collided with an iceberg on April 14, 1912, and was destroyed in the North Atlantic. The International Ice Patrol was formed in 1914 after the sinking of the *Titanic*. This group patrols the waters using planes and vessels equipped with radar and sound equipment. Using radar and computers, they also maintain a constant count of icebergs and their location, to warn ships within the area. The U.S. National Ice Center (NIC), established in 1995, monitors all icebergs worldwide using satellite sensors that check on sea ice. When an iceberg is located, the NIC names it according to its latitude and longitude. These organizations help keep the waters safe for the **maritime** community in hopes of preventing a disaster such as the *Titanic*. ⭘

QUESTIONS

1. **Which of the following best states the author's purpose?**
   - **A.** to inform the reader about the disaster of the *Titanic*
   - **B.** to explain how icebergs are formed
   - **C.** to describe the shapes of icebergs
   - **D.** to inform the reader about icebergs and their dangers

2. **Why are icebergs hazardous?**
   - **A.** They come in many different shapes.
   - **B.** Most of the ice is underwater.
   - **C.** Icebergs can travel great distances.
   - **D.** They move rapidly through the water.

3. **What is the purpose of the first paragraph?**
   - **A.** It describes why the International Ice Patrol was formed.
   - **B.** It explains the dangers of icebergs.
   - **C.** It informs the reader about the National Ice Center.
   - **D.** It describes the sinking of the *Titanic*.

4. **According to the passage, which statement is true?**
   - **A.** Icebergs are floating objects and are not visible from the surface.
   - **B.** The NIC was created as a result of the sinking of the *Titanic*.
   - **C.** Tabular icebergs are peaked at the top.
   - **D.** Greenland is the source for most icebergs in the Atlantic.

5. **According to the passage, what does the National Ice Center do?**
   - **A.** The NIC uses planes to monitor icebergs and then names them according to their longitude.
   - **B.** The NIC uses planes and sound equipment to monitor icebergs.
   - **C.** The NIC names and tracks icebergs around the globe.
   - **D.** The NIC helps track ships in iceberg territory.

6. **As used in the passage, the word *maritime* most nearly means**
   - **A.** ocean.
   - **B.** ship.
   - **C.** passenger.
   - **D.** navigation.

DIRECTIONS: *Read the passage and answer the questions that follow it.*

Inside Chichén Itzá

BUILT BY THE MAYANS during the pre-Columbian period, Chichén Itzá is an intriguing remnant of a bygone civilization. The site, located on the Yucatan Peninsula in Mexico, includes many different stone buildings, such as temples, palaces, observatories, and sports arenas. In the center of the site, natural water holes, called cenotes, provided the people with plenty of water. The most famous one is the "Cenote of Sacrifice," which was the sacred place of the rain god, Chac. The Mayans would make offerings of precious stones, metals, and pottery to the god by throwing the objects into the pool from a platform. The Mayans also performed human sacrifices on rare occasions. The Mayans who lived in Chichén Itzá possessed varied talents; they were fierce warriors who also studied astronomy and engineering. They were also a religious people, as evidenced by the many gods that are **depicted** in Mayan paintings and sculptures.

While most buildings on the site were used for religious, political, economic, or scientific purposes, some structures were used for social purposes. On the ballcourts, players had to pass a rubber ball through a small stone ring without using their hands. This was a sacred game that had severe, but not yet understood, consequences. One wall painting depicts the captain of a team being decapitated. The debate remains, however, whether this is the captain of the losing team being punished or the captain of the victorious team offering his life as a sacrifice.

Located near the ballcourts is a T-shaped structure, called Tzompantli, which was used to display the skulls of enemies and sacrificial victims. The platform is approximately 197 feet long and 39 feet wide. Its central location allows for easy viewing, which would indicate that this display held special importance to the Mayans of Chichén Itzá.

When a revolt and civil war occurred in 1221, the rule of Chichén Itzá declined. Many buildings were damaged, and the rulership shifted to other locations. The site is now a World Heritage Site and a popular tourist attraction, and the Sacred Cenote remains a popular pilgrimage destination. ○

QUESTIONS

1. **Based on the passage, which of the following statements is true?**
   A. The Mayans were a peaceful people.
   B. The Mayans invented basketball.
   C. The Mayans were a ruthless people who launched violent attacks against their neighbors.
   D. The Mayans were accomplished engineers and warriors.

2. **Which of the following best states the author's purpose?**
   A. to inform the reader about popular tourist spots in Mexico
   B. to show how the Mayans worshipped many gods
   C. to show how the Mayans ruled their country
   D. to inform the reader about aspects of Mayan culture

3. **Why were the cenotes at Chichén Itzá important?**
   A. They were a water supply and a means of transportation.
   B. They were places of sacrifice and a fresh water supply.
   C. They were the object of many wars with neighboring societies.
   D. They were central to the Mayan religion.

4. **As used in the first paragraph, the word *depicted* most nearly means**
   A. made.
   B. pictured.
   C. described.
   D. invisible.

5. **Which of the following statements best describes the reason for the second paragraph?**
   A. It explains how the Mayans used the Sacrificial Cenote.
   B. It informs the reader about astrology and Mayan gods.
   C. It informs the reader about the purpose of the ballcourts.
   D. It explains how Chichén Itzá was constructed.

6. ***Answer the following question using complete sentences:***
   Why might the Mayans have constructed the Tzompantli?

DIRECTIONS: *Read the passage and answer the questions that follow it.*

Area 51

AREA 51 HAS BEEN the subject of UFO **conspiracy** theories for years. This patch of land in southern Nevada sits beside a military base and several runways and landing strips used by the federal government for classified activities. Lockheed Corporation, a leading aerospace company, has been developing many secret aircraft since World War II, some of which have been tested at this military base. Some of the aircraft include spy planes, high altitude aircraft, and stealth fighters. Area 51, surrounded by mountain ranges and lakes, borders the Nevada Test Site (NTS). Route 375, also known as "The Extraterrestrial Highway," is located just outside Area 51.

Since 1983, operations around Area 51 have been constant, and rumors about special aircraft for government agencies have been circulating. Although the U.S. federal government uses the base, it does not acknowledge or deny its existence. The base is not visible because it is surrounded by mountains and does not appear on public government maps. Area 51 and NTS are permanently off-limits to all traffic and are heavily guarded by security checkpoints. Signs warn that "photography is prohibited" and that "use of deadly force is authorized." Radar stations guard the airspace and helicopters, and armed agents meet intruders. In the desert, uniformed guards patrol the area in camouflage, Jeeps, and Humvees.

Many people have suggested conspiracy theories regarding Area 51 because the aircraft research is classified, and many people have reported UFO sightings nearby. Some people believe that alien spacecraft are examined, studied, and stored at the base. Others believe that the government secretly meets with extraterrestrials there. A widespread theory claims that Area 51 simulates the moon's environment and the moon landing was filmed there instead of in space. Although theories are prevalent in popular culture through television shows, movies, video games, and novels, none of them has been validated. What really goes on at Area 51 still remains classified and heavily guarded.

QUESTIONS

1. **Which of the following best states the author's purpose?**
   - **A.** to inform the reader about alien activities in Nevada
   - **B.** to inform the reader about a secret government base
   - **C.** to explain the presence of a governmental restricted area in Nevada
   - **D.** to describe the relationship between the Lockheed Corporation and the government

2. **Which of the following would be the best title for this passage?**
   - **A.** Area 51: The Real Moon Landing
   - **B.** Exposing Area 51
   - **C.** Legendary Areas
   - **D.** Extraterrestrial Activities

3. **According to the passage, what is Area 51?**
   - **A.** Area 51 is a mountain used by Lockheed for testing spy planes.
   - **B.** Area 51 is used by worldwide government agencies to develop military aircraft.
   - **C.** Area 51 is used by the Lockheed Corporation to develop and test aircraft.
   - **D.** Area 51 is a meeting ground for the government and extraterrestrials.

4. **Which of the following best explains the reason for the many conspiracy theories about Area 51?**
   - **A.** Many people have reported UFO sightings in the area, which led to several conspiracy theories.
   - **B.** The military started rumors, which have led to numerous conspiracy theories.
   - **C.** The government started the conspiracy theories to stop people from uncovering the truth.
   - **D.** Because activities near Area 51 are kept secret, many theories have emerged to explain the mystery.

5. **As used in the passage, the word *conspiracy* most nearly means**
   - **A.** scheme.
   - **B.** evil.
   - **C.** well known.
   - **D.** military.

6. ***Answer the following question using complete sentences:***
   Why might the government not acknowledge or deny an area that it uses?

DIRECTIONS: *Read the passage and answer the questions that follow it.*

Easter Island Heads

EASTER ISLAND, OR THE "navel of the world," as it was called by its early settlers, is the most isolated inhabited island on the planet. Before European settlers landed on the island in 1722 on Easter Sunday, the island was inhabited by native Polynesians, called Rapanui. The triangular shaped island, located west of Chile, currently has a population of 3,791. The island is famous for its moai, or large stone statues. Most of the statues were carved between 1100 and 1600 A.D. During this time, the island's resources were the most plentiful, and 10,000 to 15,000 people lived there. It is presumed that the moai were built to represent the deceased ancestors of the islanders. However, once the stones were relocated to the ceremonial sites, the moai may have also symbolized the power of living chiefs.

The moai on Easter Island are commonly called "heads"; however, the statues also feature complete, but **truncated**, torsos. The moai are monolithic statues, meaning carved from one piece of stone. Some of the massive moai are over twenty feet tall and weigh over seventy tons. Carvers, who held a high rank in craft guilds, carved the statues from compressed volcanic ash found at a quarry site called Rano Rarku. These statues must have been expensive and time consuming to build because of their size and the crafters' fine detail. Once the moai were completed, they were moved to ceremonial sites along the coast. It is believed that a system of ropes and trees was used to drag the statues.

When the Dutch navigator, Jacob Roggeveen, came to the island in 1722, many of the 887 statues were still standing. Today, 394 moai are still visible, but some have been buried up to their necks due to erosion and shifting soil, while others have toppled and lie face-down. Researchers continue to explore the island, trying to explain the purpose and ideology behind the moai and the civilization behind the mystery. ⭘

QUESTIONS

1. **Which of the following best states the author's purpose?**
   A. to inform the reader about European expeditions
   B. to inform the reader about the Polynesians
   C. to inform the reader about Easter Island
   D. to inform the reader about the moai

2. **Which of the following would be a good title for this passage?**
   A. Polynesian Statues
   B. Volcanic Rocks
   C. Monolithic Moai
   D. Dutch Discoveries

3. **What is the main purpose of the second paragraph?**
   A. It defines the word *monolithic*.
   B. It describes the construction and erection of the moai.
   C. It gives a theory on how the statues were moved.
   D. It describes the carvers who constructed the moai.

4. **Why were the moai constructed?**
   A. The moai were constructed to enhance ceremonial sites.
   B. The moai were constructed to glorify living chiefs.
   C. The moai were constructed to protect the island from European invaders.
   D. The moai were constructed to recognize ancestors and symbolize power.

5. **As used in the passage, the word *truncated* most nearly means**
   A. shortened.
   B. ugly.
   C. exaggerated.
   D. elongated.

6. ***Answer the following question using complete sentences:***
   Why might unfinished statues exist on Easter Island?

DIRECTIONS: *Read the passage and answer the questions that follow it.*

Nelson Mandela: A Man of Principle

NELSON MANDELA, who was born in 1918, was the first democratically elected black president of South Africa. He is also a legendary figure of the African National Congress (ANC), a nonviolent civil rights group that opposed apartheid. During apartheid, the white minority had control over the government. They practiced racial segregation and discriminated against non-whites. However, Mandela began to organize attacks against the government after peaceful demonstrators were being massacred. He founded an armed wing of the ANC called "Spear of the Nation" that waged **guerilla** warfare against the apartheid regime, which used regular, uniformed soldiers. In 1963, Mandella was arrested for sabotage and conspiracy against the government. He was sentenced to life in prison in 1964. While in prison, he became the symbol of the oppressed black majority in South Africa and a worldwide symbol for his firm stance against racism.

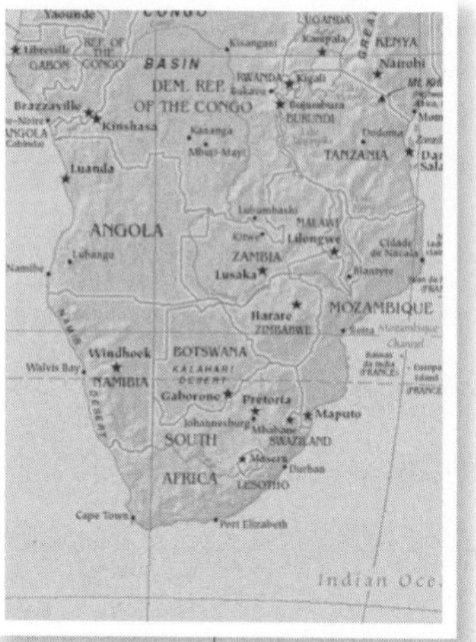

Mandela was released from prison in 1990. He was elected president of the ANC in 1991 and helped the majority regain political power. For his efforts, he received the Nobel Peace Prize in 1993. He was elected President of South Africa in 1994 and served for five years. This election was the first truly democratic election for South Africa. After retiring from the presidency, Mandela became an advocate for social and human rights organizations. After retiring from public life in 1999, he realized that he could accomplish a great deal more and entered into the fight against HIV/AIDS in Africa. In addition, Mandela opposed war of all kind, including intervention in the Balkans and the Iraq War. At age 85, he declared that he would "retire from retirement" and withdrew from public appearances. He continued to meet with world leaders, but primarily in private.

After a prolonged respiratory illness, Nelson Mandela died in December 2013. His accomplishments in easing human suffering and raising individual freedom through nonviolence are considered equal to Mahatma Gandhi's and Martin Luther King's.

QUESTIONS

1. **What can you infer that is not directly based on the facts in the passage?**
   - **A.** Mandela was imprisoned for acts against the government.
   - **B.** Mandela became president after serving years in jail.
   - **C.** Mandela was a strong and determined man.
   - **D.** Mandela always preached a nonviolent method.

2. **With which of the following statements would Nelson Mandela have most likely agreed?**
   - **A.** People need to stand up for themselves only if their opinions are right.
   - **B.** You should stand up for what is right only if it is also popular.
   - **C.** People should not speak out against the government.
   - **D.** You should stand up for what is right even if doing so causes great difficulties.

3. **Which of the following best describes the reason for the second-to-last paragraph?**
   - **A.** It describes Mandela's life before prison.
   - **B.** It describes Mandela's achievements and commitments.
   - **C.** It informs the reader about Mandela's personal life.
   - **D.** It explains how Mandela became President of South Africa.

4. **As used in the passage, the word *guerilla* most nearly means**
   - **A.** independent.
   - **B.** military.
   - **C.** nonviolent.
   - **D.** hostile.

5. **Which of the following statements best describes Nelson Mandela?**
   - **A.** He was a man who believed in always using violent methods.
   - **B.** He fought against racial segregation and discrimination.
   - **C.** He was the first President of South Africa.
   - **D.** He was the leader of the apartheid regime.

6. **According to the passage, which of the following statements is true?**
   - **A.** Nelson Mandela retired from public life immediately after retiring from the presidency.
   - **B.** The AIDS virus is no longer a crisis in Africa since Mandela helped educate people about it.
   - **C.** Apartheid was a form of government that discriminated against the white minority.
   - **D.** Mandela was sentenced to serve life in prison for conspiracy against the government.

DIRECTIONS: *Read the passage and answer the questions that follow it.*

The Pachyderm

ELEPHANTS, ALSO KNOWN AS pachyderms, are the largest living land mammals. Four types of elephants exist today but the most well known are: the African and the Asian, or Indian. The elephant can be easily identified by its tusks and long trunk, which features nostrils at the end for breathing and a long **appendage** used for picking up small objects. The hollow, flexible trunk is used to pick up food and draw water, both of which are dropped down the elephant's throat. Elephants use their trunks, which can make a variety of noises, to spray their bodies with water and dust to keep cool. In addition, elephants can cool down by flapping their large ears vigorously. Asian and African elephants can be distinguished by the size and shape of their ears. The African elephant's ears are much larger than the Asian's, measuring approximately forty-two inches in diameter. The animal's tusks are used for defense and digging roots from the ground. The Asian female elephant, however, does not have tusks.

Elephants are social animals that live in herds of up to 100 members. Although the herd consists of males, females, and babies, it is predominantly female because the males tend to live solitary lives. All the females in the herd help a mother after the birth of a calf, which often becomes the center of attention. Calves are born after a twenty-two-month pregnancy and weigh approximately 250 pounds; they are nursed for five years. Elephants are born with few survival instincts and rely on older females for guidance.

People have used elephants for centuries. Poachers have hunted elephants for their ivory tusks, which are used to make carvings and tools. Indian elephants are used for labor, especially to move timber. They have also been used in times of war; in fact, they are still ridden by important political and military figures on significant occasions. It is worth realizing that although these animals have been put to work, used in circuses, and kept in zoos, they are not truly domesticated. Unfortunately, their numbers are dwindling, quite possibly due to human interference, but they are currently a protected species, and numerous groups are working to preserve these fascinating mammals.

QUESTIONS

1. Which of the following best states the author's purpose?

A. to explain how elephants are used by humans
B. to describe the differences between the African and Asian elephant
C. to inform the reader about African and Asian elephants
D. to inform the reader about the social aspects of the herd

2. How would the author of the passage define "social animals"?

A. Social animals live together and take care of each other.
B. Social animals interact and cooperate with humans.
C. Social animals live in one area all their lives.
D. Social animals protect their young.

3. Which of the following best describes the reason for the second paragraph?

A. It describes the gestation period of baby elephants.
B. It describes the lifestyle of male elephants.
C. It explains the social aspects of a herd.
D. It mentions the dominance shown by female elephants over males.

4. According to the passage, what do humans commonly use elephants for?

A. Elephants are hunted for food.
B. Elephants are used for warfare and entertainment.
C. People sometimes abuse elephants while trying to domesticate them.
D. People are trying to preserve their natural habitats.

5. Which of the following statements best describes the reason for the first paragraph?

A. It describes the difference between the Asian and African elephant.
B. It explains how elephants cool themselves.
C. It informs the reader about the trunk.
D. It describes how the elephant uses various body parts.

6. As used in the passage, the word *appendage* most nearly means

A. organ.
B. growth.
C. organism.
D. piece.

DIRECTIONS: *Read the passage and answer the questions that follow it.*

Buried Alive

HAVE PEOPLE REALLY been buried alive? Undoubtedly, yes. Documentation since Plato's time proves that, throughout history, numerous living people have been assumed dead and buried prematurely. Edgar Allan Poe, a famous writer, dealt with it in his story "Premature Burial." In the piece, Poe describes many examples associated with all kinds of events, from political actions to natural disasters. Although they are almost impossible today, premature burials were very real possibilities in the past.

During the seventeenth century, many people suffered from plagues, cholera, or smallpox. These diseases often made people collapse or suffer comas and appear dead. While this may have been the peak of premature burial, numerous other cases have been documented. Most premature burials were accidental; however, many people were buried alive **deliberately**. For example, during medieval times, nuns and monks were buried alive as a punishment for breaking their vows. The Romans constructed special rooms for punishment. They held a religious ceremony and said prayers before putting the criminal into his or her grave. In other cultures, people were sometimes buried alive to serve the dead "in the next life."

The fear of premature burial has inspired new preventive technologies and methods to ensure that it does not happen. In a wake, people would often sit with or check on the deceased from the time of death until burial to be sure he or she was truly dead. Some chose to write special instructions in their wills, such as requesting to be stabbed or decapitated after death. Others wanted to be buried with weapons. In 1897, inventors began applying for patents for special coffins. These devices allowed a person who had been buried alive to signal for help by pulling on a cord, which was attached to a bell above ground. Although the "life-signaling coffin" originated in Belgium, patents soon spread in the U.S. More advanced technologies, such as working phones, have been sold in coffins as recently as the 1990s. Obviously, the fear that Poe exposed so vividly is still alive today. ⭘

QUESTIONS

1. **Which of the following would be the best title for this passage?**
   A. Premature Burial
   B. Poe's Version of the Afterlife
   C. Life-Signaling Coffins
   D. The Myth of Premature Burial

2. **Which of the following best states the author's purpose?**
   A. to explain an irrational fear
   B. to describe the reasons for and methods of preventing premature burial
   C. to inform the reader about cultural burial practices
   D. to describe the reasons why people were buried alive

3. **Which of the following best describes the reason for the second paragraph?**
   A. It explains why people are afraid of being buried alive.
   B. It provides some reasons why people were buried alive.
   C. It describes the way broken chastity vows were punished.
   D. It describes how plagues affected people's health.

4. **As used in the passage, the word *deliberately* most nearly means**
   A. accidentally.
   B. forcefully.
   C. intentionally.
   D. hastily.

5. **Which best describes the reason for the last paragraph?**
   A. It explains why wakes are still held today.
   B. It explains why people wrote wills.
   C. It shows how burial technologies have changed.
   D. It shows that people fear they may be buried alive.

6. **According to the passage, which of the following sentences is true?**
   A. Edgar Allan Poe's "Premature Burial" was the first documentation of people being buried alive.
   B. Nuns and monks are buried alive nowadays if they break their vows.
   C. The first "life-signaling coffin" was created in Belgium.
   D. It is absolutely impossible for people to be buried alive today.

DIRECTIONS: *Read the passage and answer the questions that follow it.*

Evita

EVA PERÓN, BORN MARÍA EVA DUARTE on May 7, 1919, was the fourth child of Juana Ibarguren and Juan Duarte. They lived in a ramshackle house 150 miles west of Buenos Aires, Argentina. Eva moved to Buenos Aires at the age of fifteen and became a radio soap opera star and performed in B-rated movies.

Eva met Col. Juan Perón during an earthquake relief meeting. They married in 1945, and she helped him become president of Argentina. In 1946, she became the First Lady of Argentina. Evita, as she was called by the people, had a fierce desire to help people who were suppressed in her country. Evita created a foundation that fought for the poor, provided healthcare, and built schools and hospitals. The Female Perónist Party, over which she presided, earned women the right to vote. The people of Argentina **revered** her as a saint for the working class. Given the title, "Spiritual Leader of the Nation," she rivaled Christianity's Virgin Mary.

Eva Perón died on July 26, 1952, from cervical cancer. Her husband hired a doctor to embalm her body. After being displayed for viewing, Eva's lifelike body was moved to the Confederation of Labor Headquarters. Plans were made to build a monument, taller than the Statue of Liberty, in her honor. However, a military coup, in 1955, overthrew Perón and forced him into exile in Madrid, Spain. Evita's body was taken secretly by the dictatorship and buried in Milan, Italy, under the name Mari Maggi. She stayed there for sixteen years until her body was transferred to Spain. Juan Perón became president of Argentina again in 1973, but died while still in office the following July. For a brief time, Eva's and Juan's bodies were displayed together in Buenos Aires. In 1976, Evita's body was finally buried in Recoleta Cemetery. Remarkably her body was so well preserved that it still appeared lifelike twenty-four years after her death. ⭘

QUESTIONS

1. **Eva Perón became a legendary figure for which of the following reasons?**
   - **A.** Hers is a fascinating story of a woman who overcame tremendous odds.
   - **B.** After her death, she remained so popular that her body was on display for twenty-four years.
   - **C.** She used her role in politics to better the lives of others, not merely her own.
   - **D.** She was revered by the people of Argentina.

2. **Which of the following best states the author's purpose?**
   - **A.** to show how someone can go from poverty to the presidency
   - **B.** to explain how Evita helped the wealthy people in her country
   - **C.** to describe the changes in Argentina during Perón's time
   - **D.** to describe the life of Evita and the unusual journey of her body

3. **The second paragraph's purpose is to**
   - **A.** describe Eva's political works and how she was viewed.
   - **B.** explain how women won the right to vote in Argentina.
   - **C.** describe how Juan Perón became president of Argentina.
   - **D.** show how Eva was opposed to Christianity.

4. **As used in the passage, the word *revered* most nearly means**
   - **A.** admired.
   - **B.** hated.
   - **C.** worshipped.
   - **D.** believed to be.

5. **Which best describes the reason for the first paragraph?**
   - **A.** It describes Eva's life before politics.
   - **B.** It explains how Eva met Juan Perón.
   - **C.** It informs the reader about Eva's low status as a poor child.
   - **D.** It explains why Eva traveled to Buenos Aires.

6. **According to the passage, what happened to Evita's body after her death?**
   - **A.** Evita was put on display in a monument larger than the Statue of Liberty.
   - **B.** Evita's husband had her buried in Italy to protect her body until he could regain the presidency.
   - **C.** Evita's body was buried next to her husband's in Recoleta Cemetery.
   - **D.** Evita's body was moved to several locations before finally being put to rest.

DIRECTIONS: *Read the passage and answer the questions that follow it.*

A Spanish Ally

BERNARDO DE GÁLVEZ WAS BORN on July 23, 1746, in a mountain village in Spain. His father, Matías de Gálvez, and mother, Josepha Gallardo, were **distinguished** members of the Spanish monarchy. Bernardo de Gálvez followed the family tradition and entered the military. In 1796, de Gálvez went to New Spain, part of North America, became the commander of the army there, and fought against the Apaches. He returned to Spain in 1772 and spent the next three years studying military science in France.

In 1776, Bernardo de Gálvez became Colonel of the Louisiana Regiment in the United States. The next year, he became the state governor. During this time, de Gálvez corresponded with Patrick Henry, Thomas Jefferson, and other patriots. De Gálvez secured the Mississippi River so only American, Spanish, and French ships could travel and send vital supplies on it. When Spain declared war on Great Britain in 1779, de Gálvez was ordered to conduct campaigns against the British along the Mississippi River and Gulf Coast and secure the territory. His men defeated the British in battles at Manchac, Baton Rouge, and Natchez. Later, he led 7,000 men in a two-month campaign that captured the British capital in Florida, which also helped win the Revolutionary War.

The war for American Independence ended in 1783, and Bernardo de Gálvez helped draft the treaty that ended the war. In 1785, his father died. After returning to New Spain, de Gálvez took his father's title of Viceroy and helped the people of Mexico during many difficult times. Bernardo de Gálvez died from a sudden illness at the age of thirty-eight, but will long be remembered as a Spanish hero in the American Revolution.

QUESTIONS

1. Which of the following best states the author's purpose?

A. to discuss reasons for the American Revolution
B. to describe an important figure in the American Revolution
C. to inform the reader about Spain's territories in America
D. to explain why the Spanish army fought Great Britain

2. Why is Bernardo de Gálvez remembered as a hero of the American Revolution?

A. He fought for his and America's cause and helped draft the treaty that ended the war.
B. He rose rapidly through the ranks from colonel to governor and was admired by his men.
C. After the war, he returned to New Spain and helped the people of Mexico.
D. He secured the Mississippi River so that ships could carry supplies inland.

3. Which of the following statements best describes the reason for the second paragraph?

A. It mentions important American political figures.
B. It describes how de Gálvez fought against America.
C. It explains when and why Spain declared war on Great Britain.
D. It describes how de Gálvez assisted America.

4. As used in the passage, the word *distinguished* most nearly means

A. ordinary.
B. wealthy.
C. famous.
D. violent.

5. Which statement best describes Bernardo de Gálvez's career?

A. He was a military leader for Great Britain.
B. He was a member of the royal monarchy.
C. He was an ally to New Spain.
D. He helped American independence.

6. Why was Bernardo de Gálvez an ally to America?

A. because America and Spain were both fighting against Britain
B. because King Carlos III commanded Bernardo de Gálvez to help America
C. because he wanted to be friends with famous American political leaders
D. because he was a traitor to Spain

DIRECTIONS: *Read the passage and answer the questions that follow it.*

The Ear

ALTHOUGH MOST PEOPLE have not stopped to think about it, the ear is an amazing organ. Not only does it enable hearing, but it also plays an important part in maintaining balance. The *outer ear*, which is the visible portion, is made of skin and cartilage. It extends from the side of the head and includes the outer ear canal. At the end of the canal lies the eardrum, which separates the outer and middle ear. The *outer ear* collects sound, which travels down the canal to the eardrum.

The *middle ear*, which is an air-filled chamber behind the eardrum, contains three small bones: the hammer, the anvil, and the stirrup. Sound waves cause the eardrum to vibrate, which then causes the bones to come in contact with one another. Together, the bones carry the vibrations from the eardrum into the *inner ear* through an opening called the *oval window.* The chamber in the *middle ear* is connected to the throat by a tube, the Eustachian tube. This tube acts as an equalizer by keeping the air pressure in the ear the same as the surrounding air pressure. If pressure outside the ear becomes greater than the pressure inside, the eardrum could burst.

The *inner ear,* which looks like a snail shell, is a fluid-filled passage. The passage contains a membrane that contains two rows of hair cells, which are connected to **auditory** nerves. Vibrations cause the fluid and hair cells in the inner ear's membrane to move. When the hair cells move, auditory nerves send impulses to the brain where they are interpreted as recognizable sounds.

The *inner ear* also houses the *semicircular canals,* which help maintain balance. The canals, which form right angles to each other, sit vertically and horizontally. The canals are filled with fluid and lined with hairs. When the head and body move, the fluid moves and causes the hairs to bend. When this happens, nerves send messages to the brain to provide balance and orientation information to the rest of the body.

QUESTIONS

1. **Which of the following best states the author's purpose?**
   A. to inform the reader about one of the five senses
   B. to explain how people keep their balance
   C. to describe the functions of an important organ
   D. to explain the different parts of the ear

2. **Which of the following would be the best title for this passage?**
   A. The Ear's Role
   B. Finding Your Balance
   C. The Inner Ear
   D. How Senses Work

3. **What happens when pressure in the middle ear does not equal that of the outer ear?**
   A. The eardrum could burst.
   B. Fluid drains through the Eustachian tubes.
   C. Sounds cannot be communicated through the nerves.
   D. Balance is lost.

4. **According to the passage, what is the purpose of the *outer ear*?**
   A. The outer ear houses the eardrum.
   B. The outer ear contains the semicircular canals.
   C. The outer ear traps sound so it can move inward.
   D. The outer ear has auditory nerves within the skin.

5. **As used in the passage, the word *auditory* most nearly means**
   A. sensitive.
   B. hearing.
   C. microscopic.
   D. interior.

6. ***Answer the following question using complete sentences:***
   Why is the ear an important organ?

DIRECTIONS: *Read the passage and answer the questions that follow it.*

Lewis and Clark

ON APRIL 30, 1803, THE U.S. government purchased a fifteen-million-dollar piece of land from France. This parcel of land, known as the Louisiana Purchase, doubled the size of the country, and included the area between the Mississippi River and the Rocky Mountains. It also extended from the Gulf of Mexico to the Canadian border. Soon after the purchase, Meriwether Lewis and William Clark set off to explore the new territory. Thomas Jefferson, the President at the time, wanted to find a land route to the Pacific, claim the Oregon territory, and obtain information about the inhabitants in the area.

The expedition officially began on May 14, 1804, when the group of approximately forty men set out along the Missouri River and went westward. In 1805, the group, called the Corps of Discovery, reached the Three Forks of the Missouri River, which they named after three political leaders including Jefferson. When they reached the top of the Jefferson, the men visited with Native American tribes, and spent the winter at Fort Mandan, in present-day North Dakota. During this time, the expedition added a valuable human resource: a Native American woman named Sacagawea. As the only woman on the trip, she is famous for being a guide and translator for the expedition. Sacagawea was a member of the Shoshone tribe and was the slave wife of French-Canadian Toussaint Charbonneau (who also joined the expedition). Her most valuable contribution, perhaps, was made when she was able to **procure** horses from the Shoshone so the expedition could travel through the steep Rockies.

Following the Missouri River, the Corps journeyed through what is now Kansas City, Missouri, and Omaha, Nebraska. After crossing the Rocky Mountains, they traveled the Clearwater River, the Snake River, and the Columbia River. After passing Celilo Falls and Portland, Oregon, they reached the Pacific Ocean in December of 1805. After a bitter winter, they journeyed home and arrived on September 23, 1806.

The journey proved to be beneficial for the United States in many different ways. The extensive sketching of the geography of rivers and mountains helped form new maps. The expedition also documented the discovery of more than 100 previously unknown plants and animals. Most importantly, however, the expedition led to a greater awareness of the land we inhabit and opened the doors to the resultant westward expansion. ◘

QUESTIONS

1. **Why was the Corps of Discovery sent on an expedition?**
   - **A.** to establish relationships with the Native Americans
   - **B.** to explore the new territory
   - **C.** to open new trade routes
   - **D.** to determine the exact location of the northern border

2. **Why was Sacagawea important to the expedition?**
   - **A.** She knew the dangers of the land and could ensure safe passage.
   - **B.** She could speak English and translate for her husband.
   - **C.** She knew how to find food in the wilderness.
   - **D.** She could translate and get what the expedition might need.

3. **What is the purpose of this passage?**
   - **A.** to reveal the valuable results of the Lewis and Clark expedition
   - **B.** to discuss Sacagawea's importance in American history
   - **C.** to reveal how difficult it was for the Corps of Discovery to trek west
   - **D.** to expose Lewis and Clark's failings

4. **Which of the following was an unexpected outcome of the expedition?**
   - **A.** crossing The Rockies on horseback
   - **B.** finding the Pacific Ocean
   - **C.** discovering new plants and animals
   - **D.** establishing relationships with Native American nations

5. **As used in the passage, the word *procured* most nearly means**
   - **A.** found.
   - **B.** stole.
   - **C.** traded.
   - **D.** obtained.

6. **According to the passage, which of the following is true?**
   - **A.** The Corps reached the Pacific in 1804.
   - **B.** Lewis and Clark named the three forks of the Missouri River after important political leaders.
   - **C.** Lewis and Clark established lasting, beneficial relationships with Native American nations.
   - **D.** The Nebraska Purchase initiated the Lewis and Clark expedition.